FAT SO?

THINK
BOOKS

A THINK Book

First published in 2006 by

Think Publishing
The Pall Mall Deposit
124-128 Barlby Road, London W10 6BL
www.think-books.com

Distributed in the UK and Ireland by Macmillan Distribution Ltd.
Brunel Road, Houndmills, Basingstoke RG21 6XS

Author: Susannah Jowitt
Editor: Jo Swinnerton
Sub Editor: Rica Dearman
Design: Lou Millward, Dominic Scott

A CIP catalogue record for this book is available from the British Library.

ISBN-10: 1-84525-012-5
ISBN-13: 978-1-84525-012-6

Printed in Italy by Grafica Veneta

Cover image: Sim Canetty-Clarke (www.simphotography.com)
Illustrations: CartoonStock Ltd

I am constantly in
The mood
For food.

Ogden Nash

THANKS

Must go to the librarians at the British Library who patiently put up with my ever-more frustrated requests for up-to-date information; to Susannah Herbert, for her invaluable help with my researches; to Emma Jones and Jo Swinnerton at Think Publishing for their patience; and to my family, especially my very fattening husband Anthony (he spoils me). I blame Adelaide (4) and Winston (2) for those two extra tyres around my middle, but they, like the Bounty bars I still have cravings for, are just too irresistible for the rest to matter. Finally, I would like to thank Maria for keeping me headed in the right direction… once more round the block, and then 60 sit-ups on the fit ball.

FOREWORD

We are all fat. I am fat. Every single woman I know is fat. Because even if we're not, we think we are. I mean, I know I'm fat, but I have it on good authority that even my friend who has the perfect vital statistics, not an inch of wobble anywhere on her and who works out at least once a day, even she has body issues and is on a permanent diet. 'The scales mean nothing,' she argues, when I point out (through gritted teeth) that she is, by any scale of measurement, annoyingly gorgeous and slim, 'I know how I want to look in clothes and I'm not there yet. But apparently, there's this great new diet…'

The gritted teeth through which I hiss when I speak to my thin-but-no-we're-fat friends would be useful in other areas of my life. Perhaps wiring my jaw would stop the intake of evil foods that seem to jump up and down for attention whenever I even contemplate how, exactly, I am going to lose weight. One certainty seems to be that, the more people think about dieting, the more difficult it becomes to lose weight. Certainly that seems to be the case in the world of statistics: we're dieting more – and getting fatter.

Who made us this way? We can blame celebrities who are touted as our 'ideal', but who are routinely underweight and unnaturally skinny in their quest for photogenic perfection. We can blame the government for feeding our schoolchildren utter rubbish. We can blame our ancient ancestors for creating metabolisms that close down in fear of famine whenever we diet. We can blame diet gurus and hack 'nutritionists' for giving entirely conflicting, permanently contradicting and almost immediately obsolete dietary advice for the worst possible diet confusion.

Oh, what the heck, let's blame all of them. And let's have a laugh while we're at it. After all, if you pick up this book, read it while walking around your kitchen trying not to think about opening the fridge and laugh out loud several times in as energetic a way as possible, well, you'll lose weight. Bargain!

Susannah Jowitt, 2006

CONTENTS

INTRODUCTION

Diet, n. – the all-consuming obsession with the food you shouldn't have eaten yesterday but did, the food you have eaten today but shouldn't have, and the food you shouldn't eat tomorrow but probably will.

The I Hate To Diet Dictionary

When Eve said to Adam, 'How about some fruit, dear?' she was promptly labelled a temptress and both were thrown out of the Garden of Eden and told to cover up their nakedness. These days, God would have patted her and Adam on the back for watching what they ate. He might even have decided not to tick her off about the weight she'd put on – all that nectar and ambrosia, without even a decent workout – which was no doubt the real reason why the Original Couple were told to get some clothes on.

Dieting is an ancient art but a modern phenomenon. A few thousand years ago, we suspect that our forebears had more pressing things on their mind than whether to eat carbohydrates after 9pm. Self-esteem was more about not letting your mate eat his first-born (the reason, we are told, that newborns look so like their dads in the first 48 hours of their life) than about how to get the most flattering hang out of that animal skin.

Now the Western world has gone diet-mad. Type 'diet' into Google and you come up with 287,000,000 websites. In 2005 alone, an astonishing 1,974 new books on diet were available from Amazon – over five per day. Nearly all are promoting one particular regime, some actively contradict one another and a few are quite clearly insane. It's hard not to think that you'd get thinner lugging this many books around than you would actually reading them.

**'I'm on three different diets.
That way I get to eat more.'**

At any one time, three quarters of women think they should lose weight. Two out of three say they are permanently trying to lose from between a few pounds to up to 18lb. But, on average, only 45% are actively dieting – and only 19% are using the 'sensible' method of eating healthily and exercising regularly. We are a culture where looks are everything – and where merely looking as if you're trying to do something about it is everything else. Enter, stage right, the idea that launched a million headlines – 'From Beached Whale to Beach Bunny in Just Six Days!', 'LoozWate: The Revolutionary Programme that Transforms Your Body in Days!'– the quick fix, the fad, the miracle and just don't mention the way the weight slaps right back on again the minute you resume normal life.

This is where *Fat, So?* comes to the rescue, with the perfect recipe for a woman of the modern age. We are a slim little thing, with a big fat heart, here to take the die out of diet, the lump out of plump, and put a hug back into huge. We'll show you that you're not alone – that the likes of Nefertiti were already beginning to consider having semi-skimmed in their asses' milk baths – and some of the crazy dietary foibles of women the world over – it's fish lips all the way if you want to fit into that cheongsam, Mrs Fu Lin. We will shine a merciless spotlight on the full panoply of diets from A-Z and stir in some full-fat, but calorie-free, comfort food in the form of some celebrity slimming stories, the where-are-they-nows of famous fat doctors and workout witches and, best of all, the news that men are now joining us in the paranoia pen.

Above all, we will not harp on, we will not preach, we will not prescribe. As Saffy says to Edina in *Absolutely Fabulous*: 'If you want to lose weight, all you've got to do is eat less and take a bit of exercise.' We are with Edina when she replies: 'But sweetie, if it was that easy, everybody would be doing it.'

38cm 39cm 40cm 41cm 42cm 43cm 44cm 45cm 46cm 47cm

AT A BOOKSHOP NEAR YOU: DIET TITLES THAT DEMONSTRATE THE ART OF THE OVERUSED COLON: HOW TO FIT AS MANY WORDS ONTO THE FRONT COVER AS THE TYPESETTER DEEMS POSSIBLE

- *Fat Is Not Your Fate: Outsmart Your Genes and Lose the Weight Forever*
- *God's Way to Lose Weight: Healthy Body, Healthy Soul Series*
- *Javalution: Fitness and Weight Loss Through Functional Coffee*
- *PeeWee Pilates: Pilates for Post-Partum Mother and Her Baby*
- *Raise the Barre: Introductory Cardiobarre: The Revolutionary 8-Week Programme for Total Mind/Body Transformation*
- *Skinny Bitch: A No Nonsense, Tough-Love Guide for Savvy Girls Who Want to Stop Eating Crap and Start Looking Fabulous*
- *The No Diet Diet: Do Something Different*
- *The Potbelly Syndrome: How Common Germs Lead to Obesity, Diabetes and Heart Disease*
- *The S.W.A.T. Workout: The Elite Exercise Plan Inspired By the Officers of Special Weapons and Tactics Teams*
- *You've Got Meal: E-musings on Dieting*
- *Only Fat People Skip Breakfast: The Refreshingly Different Diet Book*
- *The South Beach Diet: The Delicious Doctor-Designed, Foolproof Plan for Fast and Healthy Weight Loss*

38cm 39cm 40cm 41cm 42cm 43cm 44cm 45cm 46cm 47cm

BIG BRITAIN – WE ARE GETTING FATTER

- Britons spend £133bn per year on food – £3bn on fast food, £3.6bn on chocolate – but we throw a third of it away.
- In the West, we eat on average 40% more than we need to.
- A 2005 survey showed that 76% of British men over the age of 30 and 69% of women over 30 are overweight.
- Over 60% of the population of the UK is now classed as overweight or obese, including around 24 million adults.
- Excessive weight gain is now called the 'silent epidemic'. Experts are warning that within 10 to 15 years, three quarters of us could suffer the ill effects of excess weight.
- A major part of the reason is our inactivity: six out of 10 male adults don't even manage half an hour's moderate activity per day, while women are even less likely to do exercise beyond housework and walking for the bus.
- People who work at night tend to weigh more than people who work during the day.
- Where the US leads, we seem to inevitably follow and, currently, Americans consume a diet in which around 36% of their calories come from fat – the upper limit for healthy eating is 30%, preferably less.
- We are eating more fast-food meals (about two billion a year) and drinking more alcohol and sugary drinks than before; sales of sweets and snacks in Britain outstrip those in other European countries.
- Health economists estimate the obesity crisis could cost the NHS £3.6bn a year by the end of the decade.

THE BUILDING BLOCKS OF NUTRITION

There are five basic types of nutrients – protein, fats, carbohydrates, vitamins and minerals – and water. Only three nutrients – protein, fats and carbohydrates – are a source of calories. The only other source of calories – sadly, for those of us who worship at the altar of Bacchus – is alcohol, which has no nutritional value. Fats supply twice as many calories as carbohydrates or protein.

CALORIE CONTROL

When we bandy around talk of calories, technically we are talking about kilocalories, hence the confusing kCal labels on food packaging. We now depend on calorie-counting guides, but at the beginning of the line, measuring the calories of food can be done in two ways. Either you can analyse the amount of protein, fats and carbohydrates in a food and ascribe a calorific value to that (1g carbs or protein gives 4kCal, for example, while 1g fats gives 9kCal) or, more precisely and labour-intensively, use a bomb calorimeter. This precise way of measuring energy – and therefore calories – is how the fuel industries discover how much energy there is in a litre of natural gas: by burning the food in a surround of cold water and measuring the increase in temperature of the surrounding water. Technically speaking, therefore, a calorie is the amount of energy which, converted to heat, will raise the temperature of 1g of water through 1°C. So bring down your heating bill and get rid of your spare tyre at the same time, by burning that cake you wanted to eat in the immersion heater.

STUCK IN THE CHIMNEY

We think we're well-educated when it comes to diets and calorie counting, but to walk off the calories consumed at the average Christmas lunch would take a vigorous 18-mile (29km) hike.

WHY DO WE HAVE STONES AND THE AMERICANS JUST STICK TO POUNDS?

We owe the unit of stones to the Act of 1824, which established the British Imperial System, tidying up the mess that existed beforehand. However, by this time the Americans were long gone, having divorced us in the American Revolution. The Americans were always more logical than the British, so made their hundredweight (cwt) equal to 100lb, when the British one was 112lb (or 8st). And an American tonne (or short tonne) was 2,000lb, while the British is 2,240lb, not to be confused with a metric tonne which is 1,000kg. Having established these more logical boundaries (100lb in a cwt and 20 cwt in a tonne), there wasn't much room – or need – for stones in the system. Now we can just enjoy baffling them occasionally with our talk of stones – like the American friend who, when she heard someone being described as being over 13st, said: 'Wow, is she, like, a rockery?'

ADIPOSE, AVOIRDUPOIS, WHATEVER

The body's fat is found inside a type of specialised connective tissue that, taken together, constitutes adipose tissue. Also called 'fatty tissue', adipose tissue cushions the body's organs and serves as an energy source. As a sweeping generalisation, a woman of 112lb (8st) of average height will be made up of 31lb of pure adipose tissue.

LOOKING FOR A HEAVY READ?

'Fat Lit' is now weighing down our bookshelves; recent releases include *Fat Girl: A True Story*, a startlingly toxic autobiography by American writer Judith Moore. Then there's the first-person novel *The Fattest Man in America* by Christopher Nicholson, the story of a young man 'so fat he no longer looked quite human'. Another one is *The Observer* writer William Leith's *The Hungry Years: Confessions of a*

Food Addict, an excoriating ramble through the author's obsessive bingeing and bloating. None being subscribers to the mysterious, non-informative title school of thought, these are all easy to spot on the shelves if you're feeling peckish for a bit of extreme sport.

A BIRD IN THE HAND

The phrase 'eats like a horse' is obviously not something the average dieter wants to hear as a description of themselves. But just how greedy is a horse? An average 1,200lb horse eats about 15lb of hay and 9lb of grain each day if it's being fed well. This amounts to one fiftieth of its weight each day, or seven times its own weight each year. The real gluttons of the animal kingdoms – contrary to the description 'bird-like appetite' – are birds, who consume more than 90 times their own weight in food each year.

WEIGHTY WORDS

I have gained and lost the same ten pounds so many times over and over again, my cellulite must have déjà vu.

Jane Wagner

Men look at women. Women watch themselves being looked at. This determines not only most relations between men and women but also the relation of women to themselves.

John Berger, *Ways of Seeing*

There is no sincerer love than the love of food.

George Bernard Shaw

THE DIETING PHENOMENON

The number of British dieters has doubled in the past 17 years, and more are joining in every day. At the time of writing, more than 12 million men and women in the UK diet – one million of them on Weight Watchers alone. And at any one time, more than 70% of women say they are on some sort of diet.

As a society, we are basically admitting that at least one in five of us – and seven out of 10 women – has an unhealthy, addictive or obsessive relationship with food. If the same number were addicted to alcohol, that would be the sign of a terminally sick society and the government would be in a flat panic. But apart from banning the odd advertisement and making noises about improving school meals, there is still no national strategy. The government seems reluctant to mess with the billion-dollar behemoths that are the food, transport and, yes, even the diet industries that depend on people staying fat and, instead, just bombard us with advice. A Mintel survey revealed that 48% of us are fed up with healthy eating advice from do-gooders in government and charitable organisations. Seven out of 10 said the advice on binge drinking and cutting down on salt left them bewildered.

Each year we spend £2bn on diet products. In 2003, we spent £38m on self-help books alone (66% by women, 34% by surreptitious, furtive-looking men). In a recent survey, a whopping 90% of divorced or widowed women felt they needed to shed weight to stand a chance of being happy again.

However, more dieting doesn't necessarily mean healthy eating. Between 2001 and 2003, 6% of women consumed absolutely no fruit or vegetables at all. Only 11% of women diet because they want to be healthy; nearly half go on diets to wear sexy, skimpy fashion items.

A third of all women have been on diets since they were teenagers and a third admit they often put more weight back on than they lost in the first place. Only 19% use the 'sensible' method of eating less and exercising regularly.

Nearly three out of four mothers now admit passing on their worries about food to their daughters. As a result, 19% of teenage girls are overweight, but a massive 67% think they are. Eight out of 10 girls want to lose more than half a stone; 46% of these want to lose more than a stone, which would make them underweight compared to the average 14-year-old.

The sad truth is that 98% of dieters, in the long term, regain all the weight they lost on diet regimes.

38cm 39cm 40cm 41cm 42cm 43cm 44cm 45cm 46cm 47cm

THE FACTS OF DIETING LIFE

■ If you eat more calories than your body burns to keep going, surplus calories will be stored as fat.

■ The only way to remove surplus body fat (except by surgery) is to eat fewer calories than your body expends – to make up the balance, the body will then draw on its own reserves.

■ A gain or loss of weight (or, rather, fat) depends on the number of calories consumed. So even if you eat 'good' food, if you eat enough of it to ramp up the calorie count, you will not, and cannot, lose weight.

■ Technically speaking, it takes around 3,500 surplus kCal to produce 1lb of surplus body fat and the reverse to lose it; to lose 1lb, the body must receive 3,500 calories fewer.

■ The holy grail for the dieter is to find the way to marry an intake of fewer calories with a sustainable way of eating – and all without 'frightening' the body, so that it continues to draw on those fat reserves.

ORANGE-PEELING BACK THE CELLULITE

When you think of orange peel and cottage cheese, do you think of a new low-cal lunch salad or the sight of your own backside in the mirror this morning as you bent down to put on your pants? If you are a woman over 30, there's a 90% chance that you've been afflicted by cellulite – and there's a whole branch of the cosmetics industry yearning to convince you that they and they alone can shift it. Whether it's creams – on which British women spend £30m every year – or suction pads, heavy rollers, tights impregnated with caffeine capsules, Nicorette-style caffeine patches, seaweed clingfilm and mud wraps, the anti-cellulite industry prospers. And yet no one has really, so to speak, got to the bottom of it.

The word 'cellulite' was coined in the 1920s by French doctors, which means we can just about forgive them for the cruel irony of the word 'lite' appearing in something that makes us feel very heavy – heavy-hearted and heavy-bottomed. Cellulite has been around for ever – think of those Renaissance lovely ladies, peppered with the stuff. It's just more noticeable now because we show off those areas of flesh so much more.

Cellulite is the body's natural way of storing excess fat. Women have more body fat than men, so are automatically first in line for cellulite, and are more likely than men to store it in their stomach, thighs and bottom (to protect the reproductive organs), hence the tendency of cellulite to appear in those areas. Cellulite is, to some extent (and debate rages as to how far that extent goes) genetic – so blame your mum.

The appearance of cellulite – that dimpled look – is caused by fat cells protruding from the latticework, or 'honeycomb' of fibrous tissue around them. This fibrous tissue is a restraining net beneath the skin which keeps fat in place and cellulite occurs when that net barrier is ineffective and allows the fat beneath to push through.

Unfortunately for women, the fibrous tissue in the thigh is different from anywhere else, which might explain why cellulite is particularly bad in that area.

Cellulite does not differ from 'normal' fat in any chemical or molecular sense, just in the way it is held and distributed in the body tissues. Cells can swell and clump together in the dermis and hypodermis of the skin, giving rise to the characteristic bulges of orange peel skin around the bottom and thighs.

For pregnant women, the worsening of cellulite is not all to do with the actual weight gain; mothers-to-be have massive amounts of oestrogen in their systems to help soften up the fibrous tissue in the womb before the birth. The side effect is that the fibrous tissue in their hips and thighs is also weakened, allowing the fat cells to bulge through even more visibly.

Ageing doesn't help either; both the skin and the fibrous tissue on a woman's bottom and thighs loses its strength and elasticity over time, which is why cellulite is more common in women over 40.

DID YOU KNOW?

- **'Phagomaniac' is the word for someone who is mad about food.**

- **Actress Angelina Jolie has tattooed on her belly the phrase *Quod me nutrit me destruit*, which means 'what nourishes me also destroys me'.**

- **In India, a woman who wanted to make her husband obedient had to feed him a loaf of bread, the loaf made from flour that weighed the same as the wife's left shoe.**

WHAT CAN WE DO ABOUT CELLULITE?

French research has shown that 75% of cellulite appears when there is a change in the hormonal system, such as when you start or return to the contraceptive pill. This is because they mimic pregnancy and activate oestrogen-related fat storage in the lower body. So some doctors recommend speaking to your GP about one of the newer anti-bloating pills, such as Yasmin.

Smoking has been blamed for worsening cellulite. There are around 4,000 toxic chemicals in cigarettes and research has shown how these are not only stored in fat cells, but also break down the fibrous tissue holding in your fat cells.

Some scientists insist that detoxing, drinking plenty of water and, of course, investing in their particular anti-cellulite creams (avoid vague promises of 'body contouring' or 'body shaping' because these don't have the scientific confidence to even claim effectiveness against cellulite) are the best ways to rid thighs of their dimples. Others say that is bunkum and tosh – cellulite is fat, plain and simple.

It may be a case of chicken and egg, but bad circulation can cause cellulite as well as being a result of it, since the enlarged fat cells stop blood flowing properly to the danger areas of bottom and thighs. Either way, it's good to get your circulation going again, which is why the universally acknowledged treatment for improving cellulite – even if it only has a slight effect, is a good old-fashioned massage. Self-administered, 10 minutes of kneading and rolling your thighs and bottom at night (time for that Phone a Hunky Friend option) will do you the power of good. Despite the millions spent on anti-cellulite creams, in tests, none had proved more effective in shifting cellulite than a simple thigh massage.

The most common and effective active ingredient in cosmetic anti-cellulite products is caffeine. The manufacturers want us to believe that caffeine encourages the metabolism of the fats and the draining of the accumulated water from the fatty tissues – basically, liquefying fat so that it is able to burn off within the body if you exercise or cut your calorific intake. But while caffeine has been shown to shrink fat cells in a laboratory situation, there is no proof that putting it into a cream, a pair of tights or a patch and then applying it topically to the skin can actually have the same effect.

Says Dr Victor Neel, expert dermatologist at Massachusetts General Hospital in Boston: 'Caffeine has never been shown… to do anything when applied topically. Creams are a waste of money. Try not to fixate on cellulite. Just have a good diet and plenty of exercise. That's all you can do.'

WEIGHTY WORDS

Part of the secret of success in life is to eat what you like and let the food fight it out inside.

Mark Twain

Dieting is like driving with your foot on the brake. Sooner or later, the tyres wear down and we skid out of control. If diets were faulty cars, we would be suing the manufacturers. Instead, we let them blame us.

A client of Dr Rick Kausman, *If Not Dieting, Then What?*

Being fat isolates and invalidates a woman.

Susan Orbach, *Fat Is a Feminist Issue*

The slimming industry sells the obvious to the indolent.

Camilla Cavendish in *The Times*

SIX TYPES OF SLIMMER

1. Blubber clubber: The backbone of slimming clubs like Weight Watchers, Slimming World and Rosemary Conley Diet and Fitness Clubs, this is for the dieter who responds well to guidance but whose discipline goes to pot when left alone. Members pay for a weekly weigh-in with the other clubbers, and get peaks of applause for weight loss or the troughs of private shame for any gain. An expensive, time-consuming and potentially humiliating experience – after all, the practice nurse at your local health centre could do the same for free – but they continue to flourish.

2. Meal swapper: The dieter on the run who only wants to eat one meal a day, replacing the others with a milkshake, soup or other 'diet-specific' processed food. Their ability to 'eat' not just one of these shakes, but many, over a sustained period of time, is so heroic that we should vote them in for public or military service. Suffered Slim-Fast for six months? Give yourself a medal. The day you actually think of your milkshake as a real meal replacement rather than as a penance is the day that food begins to be meaningless for you. Judge for yourself whether this is a good or a bad outcome.

3. Calorie counter: The traditional dieter, who prefers meticulous calorie counting up to a daily allowance (of, say, 1,000-1,500 calories per day) to modish theories and newfangled gurus. The accountants of the diet world, equipped with calculator and books listing the calories of branded and unbranded products – these are no foodies, but those who see food as fuel. Calorie counting creates obsessives. The only thing more boring than listening to people talking about their frustrated love lives is the accompanying soundtrack of the calorie content of everything they are eating.

4. Low-fattie: Common-sense dieters who like reading labels for fat content, the low-fattie mantra could well be: 'Patience is a virtue'. Not the reckless dieting types. Trouble is, many 'low-fat' products are high-calorie as they contain a lot of refined sugars, so both weight loss and improved health might be a mirage in the long run.

5. Star-guzzler: The polar opposite of calorie counters and low-fatties, this is the unscientific approach by a dieter who has read too many trashy mags and believes that when a celebrity endorses a diet, it actually means something other than the sound of ringing cash tills. Just stop and think how much your average celeb knows about common sense, good nutrition or the demands of genuinely busy lives. Vanity holds sway over health concerns: if Liz Hurley revealed that she really kept her figure by downing a bucketful of laxatives every day, there'd be a charge of the heavy brigade towards the pharmacy counter. There are many and obvious pitfalls, not least the unrealistic expectations of weight loss within a certain miracle period. Why can celebs lose weight quicker than us mere mortals? Because they have the time, are usually thinner than us naturally anyway and, oh, they might throw up a bit on the side as well.

6. Holy detoxer: Having banned meat, dairy, wheat, processed foods, booze, caffeine or anything that makes food taste interesting, there is little left for the holy detoxer to do except proselytise about how fantastic they feel on their fruit, veg, brown rice and nasty-tasting 'detox' drink – and never mind the headaches, faintness, nausea and overwhelming tiredness, that's just the toxins being drawn out. Humour the holy detoxer: the reason you are being bored by the Sermon on the Mount is because they are so hungry that if they stop talking about how great detoxing is, they might have to eat your arm.

38cm 39cm 40cm 41cm 42cm 43cm 44cm 45cm 46cm 47cm

HOW DIETING HAS TURNED US INTO DEVIOUS LIARS

■ Of the fifth of all women who cover up their true weight, 65% of them confess that they lie to their female friends and their family. Only 6% say they've fibbed to their GP, while one in 20 have lied when registering at a gym. Bizarrely, most women will reveal their true weight to someone they've never met before and who they're unlikely to see again.

■ Only 17% of women felt their partner would be more attractive if they lost weight, yet over a quarter felt they should diet themselves.

■ In a recent survey by Adios, the natural weight-loss supplement, 11% of 18-25-year-old women admitted they'd lied to get out of events such as birthdays, weddings and dinner parties because they felt too overweight and couldn't get into their favourite outfit.

■ One in five 18-25-year-olds are likely to lie to friends and family about what they've been eating.

■ Only 17% of those who class themselves as overweight say they are honestly happy and don't care what people think.

■ One in six women admits to going to extraordinary lengths to make sure the lights are turned out during sex because they are too ashamed of their bodies and want to cover them up.

■ Half of us blame the shop when our normal dress size doesn't fit – and one in three of us say we're a smaller dress size than we actually are.

■ A staggering 20% of women confessed in a survey to having actively encouraged a friend to eat something fattening when they knew they were on a diet. A shaming 41% have even told a friend they look slim when, in reality, they don't.

■ One in seven women will stand next to an overweight person in a bar in order to make themselves look slimmer – and admit that having a fat mate makes them feel better about their own figure.

OBESITY: THE NAKED TRUTH

Obesity is a condition in which abnormal or excessive fat accumulation in adipose tissue impairs health. A person is obese if they have a body mass index (BMI) of over 30.

In the early 1980s, 8% of women and 6% of men in the UK were obese. In 2003, those figures had risen to 20% for women and 25% for men. The latest figures reveal that in the UK morbid obesity has increased by half in the last seven years to about 17 in 1,000 people – a much faster increase than for the number who are overweight. Excess weight gain in children is also increasing alarmingly. In 2002, one in five boys and one in four girls was either overweight or obese.

In 2000, more than 300 million adults were estimated to be obese; 130 million in developed and 170 million (over half the total) in other, less developed countries. Overall, the increase in obesity has been most dramatic among the more affluent populations of less developed countries – those countries said to be in transition.

There are obvious restrictions caused by obesity in mobility, organ efficiency and general quality of life; one in seven 18-25-year-olds of 2,000 surveyed women admitted that they felt too fat to run for the bus without struggling. More seriously, severe obesity is associated with a twelvefold increase in mortality in 25-35-year-olds. A recent report estimated that in England, 30,000 deaths per year are obesity related. On average, those who died from obesity-related causes had lost nine years of life. Obesity is second only to smoking as a cause of cancer and is also the most important dietary factor in cardiovascular disease and type 2 diabetes. The World Health Organisation has predicted that 300 million people will have type 2 diabetes by 2025 and that the number of deaths from diabetes will soar by 25% in the next decade. Diabetes is not confined to obesity: a woman who is only just overweight has eight times the risk of developing diabetes of someone at an ideal weight.

DIETING THROUGH THE AGES

Binge-eating was clearly an early female Neanderthal survival trait – to ensure women got enough to eat.

Comedian Emily Prager

Rather than being something you do for a couple of weeks in the hope of lifelong happiness, the word 'diet' comes from the Greek *diaita*, meaning manner of living. It referred to the manuals regulating what you ate and drank, how much you exercised and slept, and even how much sex you could have, if you were an everyday run-of-the-mill athlete in Ancient Greece.

Diet was first used in English, in the sense of deliberately starving yourself, as early as the fourteenth century. At that time, immediately after the Black Death and during medieval global warming, times were good: living labour was scarce, so peasant wages were high. Dieting became a matter of choice rather than just an everyday fact of life. But evidence of dieting – or at least, eating sensibly for both healthy and corpulence-avoiding reasons – goes way back beyond that. It seems that even the Ancient Egyptians were trying to avoid paying the wages of gluttony with their antidiabetic remedies and laxative prescriptions.

'Obesity', as a word, from the Latin *obesus*, does not show up until 1651, but medieval monks, it turns out, had already been tucking it away and giving themselves various obesity-related diseases. In fact, as you look through the years, there's rarely an age, period or even decade without something for the dieting historian to get his or her teeth into. But don't worry, this isn't a history lesson – we merely bring you morsels and titbits from down the centuries, just to reassure you there's always been someone worrying about we eat.

YOU HUNT, ME GATHER

Back at the dawn of human time, food was obviously a basic biological necessity, so Great Granny Cavewoman probably wasn't thinking too hard about how to slim down for the midsummer cave party. Through trial and error, our early ancestors learned how to identify safe sources of nutrients from among the vast array of natural products available to them as well as learning how to cope with several potentially dangerous foods and other dietary problems. The oral transmission – from mother to daughter, father to son – of such hard-won knowledge represents the very earliest form of dietary advice.

Based on the knowledge of palatable and safe foods, domestication of livestock and crops came about between 12,000 BC and 5,000 BC, marking the first real dietary change for our ancestors, as we can see from the evidence of human fossil teeth. After the hunter-gatherer stereotype of the man gorging on the occasional kill, and starving in-between (the fatty meat and offal 'feast-fast' pattern which is the basis for the Blowout Diet currently in vogue) and the woman grazing little and often, foraging on nuts and seeds closer to home (also the basis for various diets now, including the GI Diet) came, in the opinion of some nutritionists, the beginning of the 'rot': cooked foods, wheat-based foods and dairy products from domesticated animals.

WEIGHTY WORDS

Chocolate is so delicious! What a pity it's not a sin!

Marquis de Sévigné

He was a bold man that first ate an oyster.

Jonathan Swift

(EAT) PORK LIKE AN EGYPTIAN

As in so many other things, the Egyptians were years ahead of their time in many aspects of diet. Before 3,200 BC, Egypt consisted of two distinctive entities: a pork-eating North or Lower Egypt and a pork-avoiding South or Upper Egypt. Shortly after 3,200 BC, both regions were united when the Southerners invaded and conquered the North – leading to the institution of broadly-based pork avoidance throughout the Egyptian Nile valley and delta that predates the Jewish strictures on pork by more than two thousand years.

The *Ebers Papyrus*, written in Egypt around 1,550 BC, is an extraordinary collection of ancient medical texts found in Luxor in 1872. It presents 250 clinical pictures in over 800 'paragraphs' and contains what may be the first recorded diet prescription in history: the recommendation for an antidiabetic diet of wheat germ and okra. Meanwhile our own ancestors were still picking nits out of each other's hair as part of their diet.

The Greek historian Herodotus records that, during the construction of the pyramids from 3,000 BC onwards (so already ancient to him – he was going on a translation of Egyptian hieroglyphs), the construction workers were fed large quantities of onions, garlic and radishes to keep them healthy enough to complete the job. Onion was apparently recommended as a cure for a condition similar to scurvy, an idea that filtered down to other cultures and ages, but it wasn't until the twentieth century that an antibiotic preparation (Raphanin) was extracted from radish and Allicin and Allistatin from garlic and onion – so it only took five thousand-odd years for the West to cotton on.

38cm 39cm 40cm 41cm 42cm 43cm 44cm 45cm 46cm 47cm

THE HORROR, THE HORROR: DIET PILLS AND DOPE

■ The first appetite suppressant recorded was back in the third century BC when Philon the Byzantine writes about his 'hunger and thirst-checking pill', composed of sesame, honey, oil, almonds and sea onions. These days, that would be called a muesli bar.

■ In the early 1930s, Dinitrophenol was taken by thousands on the promise it would control their weight. Unfortunately, its 'day job' turned out to be an insecticide and herbicide: 12 women were blinded and others died. Extraordinarily, a variant of Dinitrophenol made a comeback in the 1980s.

■ In 1957, the injection of human chorionic gonadotrophin became the most popular medication to lose weight. Derived from the urine of pregnant women, rabbits or mares, it proved utterly useless, yet is still available today.

■ By 1970, 8% of all prescriptions were for amphetamines, for appetite suppression. Trouble was, they also raised the heartbeat, sometimes causing fibrillation, and had a range of other side effects: anxiety attacks, dehydration, even temporary insanity. In 1980, Dr Herman Tarnower, the inventor of the high-protein Scarsdale Diet, was accidentally shot to death by his girlfriend Jean Harris after she ran out of the amphetamine (Desoxyn) that he had prescribed for her.

■ In 1979, the Centre for Disease Control in the USA reported the deaths of 58 people who had taken a liquid protein formula meant to aid weight loss, made out of ground-up animal hides, tendons and bones.

■ The Cambridge Diet came in 1981, and was one of the most dangerous ever: a 320-calorie-a-day liquid diet. When the mail order version was stopped by the government after two months, the diet shifted to a pyramid-marketing scheme. Sadly, 30 people died before the government was able to shut down the diet altogether.

GREEK CHORUS

Meanwhile, over in Greece, it wasn't just Archimedean bath water that was prompting discoveries. Pythagoras, in the sixth century BC, was the first documented thinker to advocate the exact measurement of food and drink, but one of the earliest known mentions of diet therapy – to stave off and treat disease – comes in the writings of Hippocrates (he of medical oath fame) in the fourth century BC. Hippocratic followers were therefore the first to reject the notions that magical and supernatural influences determined human well-being. Almost immediately there were dietary fads, such as warriors and athletes consuming certain foods to aid athleticism and strength; lion heart and deer liver were the favoured performance enhancers of these early Olympians. By the second century AD, as compiled by Galen, the Greeks had extensive medical and dietary knowledge which dominated European thinking well into the 1600s. Especially long-lasting was the code of hygiene, ordered around the controllable aspects of a person's environment: air, food, drink, sleep, evacuation and repletion.

MARATHON BAR

Remember when the Snickers bar used to be called a Marathon? With 280 calories of nuts, toffee and chocolate? Well, before you start salivating, spare a thought for the original Marathon runner. Poor old Pheidippides didn't run 26 miles (42km) for a bit of a lark, but to announce the victory of the Greeks over the Persians to the people of Marathon. Historians reckon he expended about 2,500 calories on the effort – the equivalent of about 10 Snickers bars – which doesn't seem like much except when you consider that he was so exhausted he died on arrival. So how does Paula Radcliffe manage to survive, when there's so little of her?

Nowadays marathon runners practise a two-tier system of dieting. During training, Paula will practise 'carbo-bleeding', a low-carb, high-protein diet combined with intensive training which drains glycogen stores, making her body thin but efficient. Three days before the marathon, she will 'carbo-load' to saturate the body with energy, giving her an instant deposit of calories on which to draw for the big race, but without adding permanent bulk to her body to slow her down. If only someone had told poor Pheidippides…

PEEL ME A GRAPE, BRUTUS

Tempting as it is to ascribe a phrase that sums up all that we think indolent about the Romans, 'Peel me a grape, Beulah' was actually coined by Mae West, equally famous for debauchery, but rather more recent. It wasn't that the Romans were never gluttonous, but the Romans were equally well-acquainted with modern-day sensibility and moderation. Cicero has very modern-sounding advice on diet in old age: 'We should… use moderate exercise and neither eat nor drink more than is necessary for repairing our strength, without oppressing the organs of digestion.' Meanwhile, recent evidence shows that gladiators were 'barley-crunching' vegetarians who stuck to a diet of barley and beans in order to bulk out.

WEIGHTY WORDS

If the Venus de Milo could be animated back into life, women would only remark that her waist was large.

Ouida

To eat is a necessity, but to eat intelligently is an art.

La Rochefoucauld

ROMAN ORGY

The popular image of the Romans is that they were so decadent and debauched that they ate lying down. We know this from mosaics, but on closer examination, it turns out that this was for medical reasons. As the Roman encyclopaedist Aulus Cornelius Celsus made clear in the first century AD, there was a clear link between health and diet – and Romans thought that if they ate lying down the digestive tract would be unimpeded and therefore better for them.

The other misconception concerns the vomitorium (from the Latin *vomitus*, past participle of *vomere*, to vomit). This wasn't a room set aside to vomit in, but rather a passageway in an amphitheatre that led to the seats. The vomitoria of the Colosseum in Rome were so well designed that it's said the immense venue, which seated at least 50,000, could fill in 15 minutes. The vomitoria deposited mobs of people into their seats and afterwards disgorged them with equal abruptness into the streets – hence the name.

That's not to say the Romans were unfamiliar with throwing up, or that they never did so on purpose. Vomiting seems to have been a standard part of the fine-dining experience, which seems a shame when you look at the *Roman Cookery of Apicius* and salivate over delicious recipes. In his Moral Epistles, the Roman philosopher Seneca writes: 'When we recline at a banquet, one [slave] wipes up the spittle; another, situated beneath [the table], collects the leavings of the drunks.' OK, it doesn't actually say 'clears up the puke' but when you consider that the orator Cicero, in *Pro Rege Deiotaro*, says matter-of-factly that Julius Caesar 'expressed a desire to vomit after dinner' and elsewhere suggests that he took emetics for this purpose, we can read between the lines. Nowhere does Cicero say anything about a 'vomitorium'. Ergo, as they were wont to say up at the Senate, we can conclude that the Romans weren't shy about vomiting, and they had vomitoria – they just didn't do the former in the latter.

DID YOU KNOW?

The word 'health' in English is based on an Anglo-Saxon word 'hale', meaning 'whole'. When you consider that the English word 'holy' is based on the same root as 'hale', it becomes obvious that the two have always been entwined, as if man has always sensed that wholeness of body and wholeness of soul have been of equal importance in making life worth living.

38cm 39cm 40cm 41cm 42cm 43cm 44cm 45cm 46cm 47cm

FRIAR TUCK

The fat monk who helped Robin Hood is a part of our heritage, but how accurate a rendition could it have been?

- There are grossly obese monks carved on a choir stall seat in St George's Chapel, Windsor, shown defecating demons as a symbol of their corruption.
- Chaucer is among many medieval commentators who draw attention to gluttonous feasts in monasteries and criticise monks for sharing among themselves food that was meant to be given to the poor.
- Chronicler Peter the Venerable slated monks for 'wearing furs and eating fat'.
- At Westminster Abbey there is written evidence that even when they were 'fasting', monks were consuming more than 4,000 calories per day – up to 6,000 on normal days – with six eggs each the norm every day.
- A recent study of skeletons from three of London's medieval monasteries showed that monks were five times as likely to develop some form of obesity-related joint disease as their secular counterparts.

CHRISTIAN ASCETICISM

The Romans loved their tucker and the Greeks weren't averse to the odd banquet, so it took the Christians to come along and rain on everyone's parade. Christians were already debating the merits of various foodstuffs as early as 170 AD when an early church leader called Athenagoras settled the debate about marine fish being acceptable to eat. But it was a man called John Chrysostom, a fourth-century Christian leader, writing extensively on proper and improper diet, who first really put the boot in to 'food as fun'. He advocated reduced food intake and regular fasting as appropriate for really pious Christians, a concept with major health and nutritional implications down through the centuries. For the first time food as a general concept was being restricted – and not for health or practical reasons, but on religious grounds.

Anthimus, a fifth-century Greek physician, in *The Dietetics*, advised Christians to be moderate in eating and drinking and argued that foods should be easily and readily digested. He warned against eating eight items: bacon rind, old cheese, hard-boiled eggs, old fish, mushrooms, oysters, pickled fish and pigeon. Thereafter, fasting, hunger and asceticism became the gold standard for holiness in the Dark Ages; it went without saying that one of the first qualities of sainthood was a tendency to scrawniness. Fat was already demonised.

In 1550, an autobiographical account by an Italian called Luigi Cornaro showed how, after a lifetime of indulgence in food and wine, Cornaro was told by physicians that he would be dead by the age of 40 unless he trimmed his sails. Cornaro immediately embarked on a diet of extreme moderation, having only 12oz of food and 14oz of wine daily; whereupon he lived until well into his 90s. This proven success story of moderation was to have an influence well into the nineteenth century, when proponents of Christian temperance adopted the secular story of this early dieter for their own ends.

In 1695, when Restoration debauchery was the norm in higher society, Thomas Tyron, a prolific pamphleteer, brought out *A New Method of Educating Children*, which extolled the virtues of dietary moderation for children, believing as he did in the concept of food as nourishment for the soul as well as the body. Recommendations were specific: 'Simple meats and drinks – not too sweet nor too bitter… for all extremes beget their own qualities and complections… but gruels, paps, rice, variously dress'd are very wholsom.'

TACUINUM SANITATIS SALERNITATUM

This is the appropriately stern-sounding name for one of the most important thirteenth-century medieval texts outside the strictly religious lexicon. It is a blend of Christian and Muslim dietary traditions, and looked at food prejudices and taboos, with statements on a wide range of dietary issues ranging, as one modern commentator said, 'from the highly sensible to the absolutely crazy'. Foods to be particularly avoided were those that promoted the formation of black bile, the 'moist' one of the four mystical humours, foods described as 'enemies of the sick', like apple, cheese, goat, hare, salted meat, milk, peach, pear, veal and venison. Crocuses were one of the more unusual recommendations – good for the heart and, if soaked in raisin wine, for counteracting drunkenness.

WEIGHTY WORDS

Let me have men about me that are fat… Sleek-headed men, and such as sleep-a-nights. Yon Cassius has a lean and hungry look… Such men are dangerous.

Julius Caesar in Shakespeare's play

EASTER FEASTING

In medieval times, the Easter feast was the gastronomic highlight of the year, coming as it did after the punishing 40 days of the Lenten fast, a diet that would give even Renée Zellweger pause for thought. Since only fish had escaped God's curse, fast meant fish and, in wintertime medieval Britain, fish meant herring. The flesh of the herring stuck to the fingers and the salted skin was particularly abhorrent. One schoolboy in the 1400s wailed into his notebook: 'Thou wyll not beleve how werey I am off fyshhe, and how moch I desire that flesch wer cum in again.' Easter was the release: veal, capon, pigeon, beef, lamb and rabbit were probably the first tastes of meat for many since Christmas. Real eggs – the Countess of Leicester bought 1,000 eggs for her tenants at Dover Castle – were made into tansies, a spicy, creamy omelette. An early form of gingerbread – honey, ginger, breadcrumbs and saffron baked into a biscuit – and marchpanes (marzipan) satisfied an increasingly sweet tooth. Pain perdu, bread dipped in egg, fried in butter then dipped in sugar, was also a high-calorie favourite. It was all a long way from the Lenten fasts and even further from the strictures of the early Christians...

BLAME IT ON THE BLOKES

In the Age of Enlightenment, disease, plague and fear of famine receded leaving a society more secure and – with the rise of the empire – more confident in many things, including its food supply. From the abundance of female flesh in the paintings of Rubens, Rembrandt and, later, Courbet and Renoir, we can see that voluptuous feminine sexuality was a thing to be celebrated, not avoided; plumpness implied both prosperity and a ladylike idleness.

During the eighteenth century, women at a certain social level were being raised from their previously subservient role to one of greater equality, one where they were treated more like men. This was the age of the grandes dames of the Parisian salons, famous for their wit, charm and intelligence. They were confident in their sexuality, happy with their body shapes and generally having a fine old time.

But sexual equality was not a steadily progressing movement. As there was a backlash towards women in the early years of the nineteenth century, putting them 'back in their place', so there was a change in the ideal female body shape. The nineteenth-century lady was fragile and languorous, and her vulnerability emphasised the strength, power and superiority of the man.

Literary role models like La Dame Aux Camellias showed how the pallor of consumption, the slimness of illness, had become chic. The new heroine was too unworldly for coarse things like food, so ladies were known to take enemas or purgatives to maintain a tiny waist and the illusion that they didn't eat. Writer Hester Pendleton noted in 1863: 'Delicacy of constitution is considered a badge of aristocracy and daughters would feel themselves deprecated by too robust health.'

At the height of the Victorian period, tight corsets took over in the maintenance of those tiny waists. As the corsets got tighter and more restrictive, the less efficient the female body became in digesting her food – thereby ensuring that she ate little, if often. Even when corsets were discarded after World War I, feminists believe that it was merely 'internalised' – that, by that time, the concept of a woman's waist being narrow had become so ingrained that even when they didn't have the haberdashery to effect it, women had to try to recreate it through diet and that newfangled concept: exercise.

Today, there are opposing ideals and new confusions; some women diet to assert their sexual freedom, seeing their body as an independent tool for their use: honed, lean, smooth. Others are more rooted in nineteenth-century sensibility, dieting to show their appealing vulnerability – to be slim, soft, petted.

CAFFEINE: WONDER DRUG OR DEVIL DRINK?

In 1695, the Medical School of Paris announced that coffee deprived men of their generative powers. Coffee drinkers, it was said, just like 'self-abusers' became diminished shadows of their former selves, with haggard looks and uncontrollable tremors. Just another morning at Starbucks, then... Even by the 1990s, coffee still veered diet-wise from being bad-guy toxin to good-guy metabolism-booster, although medically, the votes were coming in for the fragrant bean.

In 1998, researchers proved that caffeine could ease tension headaches and in October 1999, research at a Texas hospital showed how both alcohol and caffeine together – an Irish coffee, perhaps – worked just as well to limit stroke damage as conventional drugs.

VICTORIAN FAST FOOD

SUGAR SUGAR

Diabetes may feel like a modern condition but it's as old as civilisation. By 600 BC, Hindu physicians had identified the clinical symptoms of diabetes and, around 400 BC, an Indian physician, Susruta, suggested it might be linked to an excess of sugar, flour and rice in the diet. Recommendations in the medical text of Caraka Samhita (c.123 AD) were for a moderate diet high in fibre and carbohydrates. But it took a while for diabetes to sink in for other cultures.

In the seventeenth century, Dr Thomas Willis noticed sweet-smelling urine in one of his very fat patients and observed: 'I do disapprove of things preserved or very much seasoned with sugar.' Willis's problem was that he was court physician to Charles II, who was enjoying much-needed revenues from the slave trade and the import of refined sugar, so to have opined about the evils of sugar would have been impolitic. These days, diabetes is not only the hidden health bomb of Western civilisation but also the ruination of cultures previously unexposed to sugar: the Indians and Zulus in South Africa; Yemeni Jews in Israel; Native Americans; Maoris in New Zealand and Polynesians in the South Pacific.

THE GOOD OLDE TUMS

A recent archaeological dig in Glasgow showed that food there was much healthier 600 years ago than it is today. Medieval Glaswegians enjoyed a diet of various meals, coarse breads, herbs, seasonal fruit and veg, washed down with organic beer – a far cry from the pizza, burgers and chips that has led to a huge rise in obesity, heart attacks, diabetes and other fat-related ailments in the city. The absence of sugar in food had another beneficial effect: their teeth were worn rather than decayed. City Councillor Catherine McMaster, who was working on the project, said: 'It seems they were into "five-a-day" 600 years before the rest of us.'

WEIGHTY WORDS

Remember, 20% of women have inferiority complexes; 70% have illusions.

Elsa Schiaparelli

BYRON, THE FIRST CELEBRITY SLIMMER

For the poet Byron, in the early 1800s, fat was a thing of horror, symbolising dullness and lethargy. As a fat child, Byron was horrified to find himself turning into a corpulent young man in his teens at which point the great 'Thinning Campaign' started: a diet of hard biscuits, soda water and potatoes flattened and drenched in vinegar. It was to go on all his life – his vanity and his tendency to put on flesh in the blink of an eye meant that it had to. At the age of 19, he weighed nearly 210lb (15st) and found himself 'gross, stupid and repulsive', but after 'violent exercise, much physic and hot baths', there emerged from the hulk of his 'natural state' a creature of 'matchless beauty'. As Walter Scott said, 'The beauty of Byron is one which makes one dream', and later, 'he is like the sculpture of a beautiful alabaster vase, lighted up from within'.

But Byron never could conceal his disgust at others less disciplined than himself. 'A woman should never be seen eating and drinking,' he wrote, 'unless it be a lobster salad and champagne, the only truly feminine and becoming viands.' Such was his magnetism that he influenced others to think the same way and, just like the celebrity slimmers of the twenty-first century, the influence wasn't exactly benign. According to American writer George Beard, 'Our young ladies live all their growing girlhood in semi-starvation' because of a fear of 'incurring the horror of the disciples of Lord Byron.'

BANTING: WHEN THE MAN BECAME THE VERB

William Banting (1787-1878) was a respectable cabinetmaker who specialised in coffins. He had originally gone to his doctor because of his poor hearing and mentioned to him, in passing, that he was worried that he could hardly bend to tie up his shoes. The doctor took one look at him, diagnosed a probable accumulation of fat around part of his hearing system and promptly put him on a low-carb diet. Banting's *Letter on Corpulence*, published in 1863, described how he'd lost 35lb of his original 202lb (14st 6lb) in just nine months, restoring his sight, improving his hearing and reducing his bulk by many inches. It was a feel-good story that resulted in the world's first diet book.

Banting talks sternly about having to 'abstain as much as possible from bread, sugar, beer and potatoes', but is not self-righteous; he talks about occasional lapses: 'if I choose to spend a day or so with Dives, so to speak, I must not forget to devote the next to Lazarus.' The book was such a bestseller and Banting himself became such a household name that even the would-be King of France, the obese Comte de Chambord, used the diet to get down to riding weight in the event that he might need to ride victoriously into Paris.

Banting, who had lost his wife and daughter just before finding fame, was resolutely unstarstruck, giving all the proceeds of the book to a series of charities for the poor. *The Times* in 1864 was the first to use to 'bant' as a new word, describing the act of dieting purely for weight control. Thereafter, in England, banting became a verb – as in: 'If I eat that large slice of cake, I shall be banting all next week to make up for it.' Interestingly, modern doctors looking at Banting's case, have concluded that he was almost certainly a diabetic. And a cautionary note for dieters: the Comte de Chambord actually died from banting too hard and too obsessively.

DISGRACEFUL GLUTTONY

We should be thankful we've only got the likes of the government and Gillian 'You Are What You Eat' McKeith to tick us off about our bad diet habits. Many were the dangers of sinful dietary overindulgence, according to the rather more fire-and-brimstone Cornelius Blatchley in 1818. The intemperate could expect to be 'afflicted with the gout, racked with the stone, cramped with the colic, drowned with the dropsy, suffocated by asthma and hydrothorax, nauseated with gluttony, vomited with drunkenness, burnt, like Aetna, with lusts or fever, shaken like Sinai with hypochondriac and hysteric terrors and perturbations, or stretched as on a rack with tetanus.'

THE HAVES AND THE HAVE NOTS: VICTORIAN DIET

Huge divisions between rich and poor made for a split diet: the amount of food eaten by the wealthy was Gargantuan and would make a modern nutritionist faint, while bread, dripping and the newly invented margarine, if they were lucky, formed the basis of the working class diet. The former suffered from liver disease, gout, heart attacks, obesity, high blood pressure, strokes and alcoholism from their rich eight-course meals of fish, meat, fowl and so on; the latter suffered rickets, tuberculosis, miscarriages, scurvy and other conditions caused by the malnutrition of not having enough nutrients, fresh veg or fruit. Shafts of light – enjoyed by rich and poor – in this diet blackspot of an era included nutritious soups, inexpensive rabbit and a smorgasbord of shellfish like cockles and oysters.

DID YOU KNOW?

M&M's were developed so that soldiers could eat chocolate without their hands getting sticky.

STAYING THIN

Just over a hundred years ago, the need to stay thin – or at least profess a desire to become thin – was the exception not the norm, in complete contrast to today. In 1890, a weight-gain advertisement for 'Fatten-U Foods' encouraged women not to look like 'those poor unfortunates who must, in the confines of the bedroom, try to cover her poor thin figure from the gaze of her beloved spouse'. But the late nineteenth century saw a sea-change in the 'social' meaning of fat in the UK. In 1880, success was still embodied in corpulence, the visible signs of prospering, and failure was suggested by suspicious emaciation. By 1900, that was beginning to change: the influx of tall, lean, fit Americans waving thick pocketbooks of cash, the rise of exercise as a leisure pursuit for both sexes and a new pseudo-Christian temperance were all as important as any scientific discoveries in reversing the image. Increasingly, fatness was equated with weakness (both moral and physical) or incapacity, slimness with physical dynamism and mental control.

In 1907, a play opened in New York called *Nobody Loves a Fat Man* with jokes directed against, among others, the portly president-to-be, Taft. At nearly 336lb (24st), William Taft was the heaviest president and once had the misfortune of getting stuck in the White House bath. At just over 98lb (7st), James Madison was the lightest president. George Bush (the elder) was such a chubby toddler that he was nicknamed 'Fatty McGee McGaw' by his father.

In Edith Wharton's novel *The Custom of the Country*, published in 1913, the heroine Undine Spragg contemplates herself in the mirror. 'She was tall enough to carry off a little extra weight, but excessive slimness was the fashion, and she shuddered at the thought that she might some day deviate from the perpendicular.' Following World War I, one of the fundamental themes of modern life had emerged: dieting, weight consciousness and a widespread hostility to obesity.

ALL IN A WORD

Looking at the emergence of vocabulary offers an insight into the developing concern for and distaste about fatness towards the end of the nineteenth century. 'Porky' started to be used as a term of derision in the 1860s; 'butterball' by 1870, 'jumbo' in 1880. 'Slob', an Irish word for a certain kind of sticky mud (interesting because it tends to be used only for overweight men) made its entry into the English language in the 1860s when the lord mayor of London was described as a 'fat slob'. By the 1880s, 'slob' was in regular use in the US.

THE CHEWING MOVEMENT

This was one of the many food fads of the late nineteenth century, started by William Gladstone, then prime minister, who claimed that to assure proper digestion he chewed each bite of food 32 times, one for each tooth. However, American businessman Horace Fletcher took this to extremes; believing that digestion took place in the back of the throat, he chewed until his food dissolved in his mouth, claiming that a shallot had once required 720 chews. So proud was he of his 'remarkably odour-free' stools that he distributed them freely by mail to would-be disciples of the movement. Come back, Gillian McKeith, all is forgiven.

NURSE KNOWS BEST

Everyone knows that Florence Nightingale founded the nursing profession, but what is less well-known is that she was one of the first to apply the art of dietetics on an institutional scale. At Scutari, during the Crimean War, Florence was so concerned about the effect of diet on recovery – and in staving off disease – that she established two extra 'diet' kitchens where facilities were dedicated to producing healthy food for the sick.

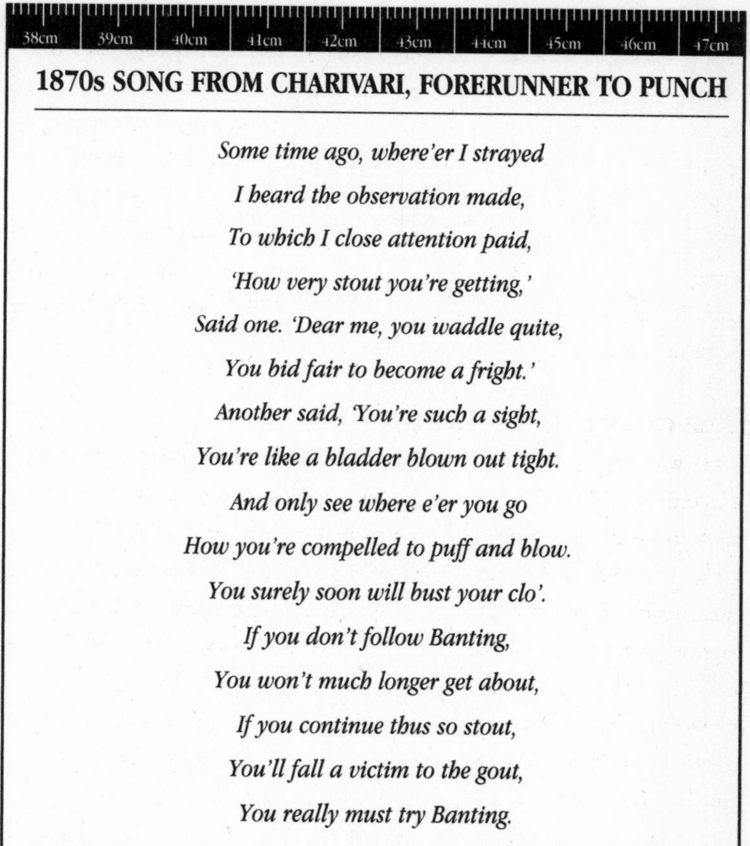

1870s SONG FROM CHARIVARI, FORERUNNER TO PUNCH

Some time ago, where'er I strayed
I heard the observation made,
To which I close attention paid,
'How very stout you're getting,'
Said one. 'Dear me, you waddle quite,
You bid fair to become a fright.'
Another said, 'You're such a sight,
You're like a bladder blown out tight.
And only see where e'er you go
How you're compelled to puff and blow.
You surely soon will bust your clo'.
If you don't follow Banting,
You won't much longer get about,
If you continue thus so stout,
You'll fall a victim to the gout,
You really must try Banting.

FUNKING IT

The term 'vitamin' was coined by the fantastically named Casimir Funk in 1912, who strangely (and annoyingly: how much more fun would it be to be told that we must top up our Funk intake each day?) did not follow the Victorian habit of coining new scientific terms using his own name. Instead he opted for a compression of VITal AMINo acid.

THE NINETEENTH-CENTURY: THE AGE OF DIETETIC DISCOVERY

■ 1827: William Prout proposed that nutrition was to be understood through three major food components which he coined as carbohydrates, fats and proteins. The great food-combining debates had only just begun…

■ 1830: Presbyterian minister Sylvester Graham, the 'father' of the modern American food fad, produced the Science of Human Life, his prescription for health and morality, in which improper diet was one of the two major dangers to a natural life (sexuality being the other one, natch). By 1835, Graham had become known across the US as the prophet of bran bread and the hater of processed white flour.

■ 1830s: John Von Liebig's view that 'muscular motion can be produced only by the oxidation of protein' provided the cornerstone for all nineteenth-century dietary recommendations: meeting the need for protein and energy. This later led to occurrences of scurvy. It wasn't until a hundred years later that Liebig's concept that protein, energy-yielding nutrients and a few minerals constituted an adequate diet were really challenged.

■ 1847: The first dietary recommendations for a specific nutrient were made by Dutch food expert G Mulder, based on his studies: 100g protein per day for a labourer and 60g for a sedentary person.

■ 1850: The American Vegetarian Society was founded.

■ 1862: Dr E Smith was asked by the British government to investigate starvation and disease during the cotton famine in Lancashire. His brief was to identify the 'least cost per head per week for which food can be bought in such quantity and such quality as will avert starvation-disease from the unemployed population'. His conclusions? That a nutritionally adequate daily diet should include 80g protein and result in 3,000 calories.

■ 1863: Banting's Letter on Corpulence is published. Foreshadowing the publishing phenomenon that was to be diet publishing in the next century, it sold 58,000 copies, a runaway bestseller.

■ 1870s: Anorexia nervosa emerged as a new disease, termed for those whose food refusal did not stem from any organic illness, but who were also not insane. The term was almost exclusively applied to young women aged 16-23. Bulimia, as a form of anorexia, was not acknowledged until 1926.

■ 1870s: The term 'calorie', previously introduced as a general heat measurement, began to be applied to the assessment of the energy capacity of foods.

■ 1876: John Harvey Kellogg took up the position of medical director at Battle Creek Sanatorium, offering diet-based health regimes, enemas, bed rest, hydrotherapy and exercise at the world's first fat farm.

■ 1880: The high-fat, low-carbohydrate diet is first proposed, in Germany – predating Atkins by nearly a hundred years.

■ 1880s: The golden age of food faddism according to some. Vehement vegetarians did battle with ardent carnivores in an attempt to gain the moral and scientific high ground on diet. Throwing in their own gauntlets were the 'no breakfast faddists', the 'raw food faddists', the 'no fermentation faddists' to name but a few. Sounds like the usual contents of The Observer's food supplement…

■ 1894: A German doctor, Max Rubner, linked the consumption of calories with the rate of metabolism.

■ 1894: Farmer's Bulletin – the first published guidance on dietary advice by the US Department of Agriculture, with a suggested diet for American males based on protein, carbs, fat and 'mineral matter'. The concept of pleasure in eating was restricted to the affluent; in the Bulletin's 'energy for work' calculations, vegetables for the working class were viewed as an inefficient source of nutrition due to their cost.

45in 46in 47in 48in 49in 50in

FLAPPING AGAINST FAT

When Agatha Christie left her husband and disappeared for 10 days in 1926, it turned out she'd gone to the health spa at Harrogate Royal Baths. While there she had a range of slightly grisly-sounding treatments involving enemas, hosepipes and even electricity while on a strict regime of lettuce and strained soup. This was all par for the course for society women in the 1920s and 1930s, when dieting became a public obsession and the fascination with one's insides reached new heights (or should that be depths?). PG Wodehouse even refers to it in *Jeeves and the Old School Chum* when Bertie Wooster moans to Jeeves about the awful diet fanatic Laura Pyke, saying how she talked about the lining of the stomach in a manner quite unsuited to mixed company. Colonic irrigation, the new Vichy hydrotherapies, steam cubicles: they were all out in the open and the gloves were off.

38cm 39cm 40cm 41cm 42cm 43cm 44cm 45cm 46cm 47cm

TEN US WARTIME FOOD POSTERS 1942-44

1. Eat fruit and vegetables
2. Carrots keep you healthy
3. Here's how to grow strong, America
4. US needs us strong
5. Milk and eggs – nature's food
6. Food is a weapon – don't waste it!
7. Jenny on the job: eats man size meals
8. Every child needs a good school lunch
9. Dig for victory
10. Fish is a fighting food

A WEIGHTY MATTER

In 1927, 40,000 public penny scales were dispersed throughout America. Although they had been available since the latter part of the nineteenth century, this surge in popularity reflected the growing belief that one should know one's own weight.

THE RISE OF FASCISM – AND FAT

The 1930s may have seen the rise of fascism but it also saw the rise of what would now be considered a similarly sinister dogma: the comprehensive belief in the goodness of animal fats. Between 1930 and the mid-1960s, the concept of a healthy diet was one that was high in fat and low in fibre. Milk and meat were believed to be protective against diseases, while carbohydrate-based foods were seen as starch-laden and fattening.

In America, a banana-and-milk diet was introduced with the blessing of the American Medical Association. Overseas, matters were more extreme. One friend of Mussolini's – the notorious Futurist poet Marinetti – called for pasta to be outlawed, claiming it made Italians too fat for the 'new heroic efforts that the race would soon require of them'. This provoked a terrible outcry – luckily brought to a close by a photo of Marinetti himself forking a large bowl of spaghetti into his mouth. In 1938, the British Medical Association recommended that the British should drink 80% more milk, eat 55% more eggs, 40% more butter and 30% more meat. The government introduced free school milk and later we 'went to work on an egg'.

WEIGHTY WORDS

People who eat white bread have no dreams.

Diana Vreeland

CHOLESTEROL KILLER

A pathologist's exercise to learn about war wounds in Korea by dissecting the bodies of dead American soldiers had an unexpected outcome. Despite the average age of the men being only 22 years old, a staggering three quarters of them showed evidence of coronary heart disease, with valves and arteries clogged with deposits of fibrous, fatty material. This was, of course, cholesterol – and only a year before in 1950, an American doctor, John Gofman, had put forward a brand-new hypothesis that blood cholesterol was to blame for exactly this: the rise in coronary heart disease as a result of the Western obsession with animal fats in their diet.

WARTIME AUSTERITY

During World War II, food and nutrition messages provided information and, at the same time, bolstered British patriotism: 'cooking and eating for victory' with recipes like leftover meat stew, pease pudding and a low-fat, low-sugar apple crumble. Food rationing started in 1940 and it wasn't until June 1954 that meat became freely available again. During that time, heart disease, obesity, diabetes and some cancers were much less common because the restriction of meat, fats and sugar improved health. If the same rationing were to be imposed today, everyone who is overweight would immediately start losing weight – with less than 30% of energy from fat, around 50% from good carbs, enough protein (just), lots of bone-building calcium, enough iron, minerals and vitamins and only 4g salt daily.

WEIGHTY WORDS

Eat… to live, and do not live to eat.

William Penn 1693

A STUDY OF THE SURVIVORS OF THE TWO YEARS OF FAMINE IN THE WARSAW GHETTO OF WORLD WAR II CAME UP WITH SOME DISTURBING IMPLICATIONS FOR LONG-TERM WEIGHT LOSS

■ It was known that the average daily calorie intake was between 700 and 800 (about 1,700 less than before the war) per ghetto inmate.

■ If the average weight of body fat and adipose tissue was about 30lb, this represents 100,000 calories available to be lost per person.

■ From a scientific point of view, a daily deficit of 1,700 calories means a total deficit, over the years, of one million calories.

■ So what happened to the remaining deficit 900,000 calories?

■ Meanwhile, of the survivors of the Warsaw Ghetto, nearly all of whom also went through the starvation of the concentration camps, most of those who resumed sedentary lives did become fat after the war – flabby rather than heavy, with devastated muscle tone.

■ The conclusion: when faced with a low-calorie intake, the body goes into 'famine' mode, secreting fat stores and eating into muscle tissue instead. Once normal calorific intake is resumed, the body does not replace the burned muscle tissue but, assuming that starvation might happen again any minute, whacks any surplus calories straight into fat cells. Because the metabolism is so slow after years of low calories, there will be more surplus calories than before and therefore more fat cells.

■ The implication: that dieting makes you fat, by 'frightening' your body into famine mode, whereby an increased rate of surplus calories are stored as adipose tissue.

WARTIME DISCOVERIES

It often takes times of stress or deprivation for a previously unnoticed phenomenon to float to the surface... in this case, the existence of 'good' carbohydrates. In the overwhelming bloodshed of World War I, it wasn't immediately noticed that the national canteens established in Belgium during the war, and the consumption of large quantities of whole cereals and potatoes, had led to a dramatic drop in infant and civilian adult mortality.

But when shortages of food in Denmark during the same war forced the Danes to eat, similarly, whole grains and potatoes (foods previously earmarked for cattle and swine) and there was an identical drop in mortality and rise in health, health professionals started to ponder.

During World War II, the people of Singapore in 1941-1942 faced acute food shortages and were compelled by the British authorities to eat brown rice (because the process of refining and polishing the rice resulted in nearly a third of the grain being thrown away). In one year, infant mortality had halved. On the Burma line, brown rice and bran usually fed to pigs was fed to the Allied prisoners building the railway – yet despite the terrible privations and intense stress, no prisoners got stomach ulcers.

Meanwhile up in Hong Kong, where the prisoners were fed white rice in relatively stress-free conditions, stomach ulcers were common. When some Hong Kong prisoners were moved to Tokyo and fed brown rice in terrible conditions (because of the intense bombing, white rice was at a scarcity and the blitz was exhausting), those stomach ulcers vanished. Yet it wasn't until the 1970s that there was any real flurry of excitement about carbohydrates and only relatively recently that carbohydrates have been thoroughly disentangled into 'good' simple carbs and 'bad' complex carbs for both health and weight-loss purposes.

INTOXICATING STUFF

In a story from *Punch*, when the Queen asked for a glass of wine at lunch, the Queen Mother reportedly asked her, 'Is that wise? You know you have to reign all afternoon.' But it was only towards the end of the twentieth century that alcohol became the 'Public Dieting Enemy No. 1' – no longer something to be abstained from on a fast, but given up entirely in the new 'lifestyle' approach to weight loss.

We search for stories like 'Red Wine Wards Off Cancer', or 'Vodka Has A Fraction of the Calories', but the simple truth is that alcohol is now persona non grata at the dieter's table. The alcohol industry responds by making alcohol ever sweeter and more fattening. The pundits say it's to pull in the younger punters, but we know a more exquisite agony: the lure of alcohol and the pull of the sweet tooth, combined for extra toughness. Thank you, drinks industry.

38cm 39cm 40cm 41cm 42cm 43cm 44cm 45cm 46cm 47cm

CHILDREN IN THE 1950S, DESPITE THE FOOD SHORTAGES OF THE POST-WAR PERIOD, ATE BETTER

- Ate more bread and milk, increasing their fibre and calcium intake
- Drank few soft drinks, deriving less of their energy from sugar
- Got their vitamin C from vegetables rather than juices and drinks
- Ate more red meat, giving them more iron
- Had more fat in their diet

DID YOU KNOW?

Miss Piggy's vital statistics are 27-20-32.

38cm 39cm 40cm 41cm 42cm 43cm 44cm 45cm 46cm 47cm

BRITISH FOOD CONSUMPTION IN THE 1950s

- 2.716 litres of milk
- 3.5 eggs
- 329g cooking fat and oil
- 1.6kg bread
- 190g cakes and pastries
- 206g flour
- 331g fruit – 93g citrus fruits, 201g apples and pears, 37g bananas
- Income spent on food and non-alcoholic drinks = one third

(all figures per person per week)

FLOWER POWER FOOD

As in so many spheres of the 1960s, technology, (or, in this case, chemistry) some knowledge and the feeling that all paradigms were shifting led to a flowering of diets, regimes and – a new word – lifestyles. One particular legacy of the flower-power era stemmed from the flower children's deification of poverty. This glorification of all that went counter to the commercialism and modernism of the profligate West was reflected in lentils, brown rice, wholegrains – foods endowed with an aura of spirituality through association with Third World poverty and Asian gurus to whom so many of the 1960s kids attributed great and disinterested wisdom. Even when the hippies rejoined the commercial rat race and gave up their communes for houses and their freedom for wages, they continued to eat 'health foods' as if to compensate for the outward loss of their ideals. Man.

Meanwhile, in more conventional circles, a Brooklyn housewife called Jean Nidetch, sat down in 1963 and started what was to be the largest, best-known weight-loss organisation in the world, from her living room: Weight Watchers.

I CAN NEVER REMEMBER NAMES
... DO YOU MIND IF I JUST CALL YOU
"FAT BASTARD"
FRAN

THE SEVENTIES: THE CONSTIPATION CONTROVERSY

The shifts in dietary thinking in the West during the 1970s could be known collectively as the 'Bowel Movement'. As the demographic shift of a population no longer so much at the prey of world wars and disease epidemics resulted in an increase of people living over the age of 65, there was a shift in health policy of the developed nations towards the prevention of chronic and degenerative diseases.

Suddenly, cardiovascular disease and cancer now accounted for 70% of deaths, compared to 20% at the turn of the century and Western dietitians were beginning to shift uncomfortably in their seats at the increasing reports linking type and quantity of fats with mortality from heart disease. Advice was to centre on avoiding foods that were deemed bad. Americans now began to look at a plate of ham and eggs – which had been the nation's favourite restaurant dish in 1942 – as a sodium-packed, cholesterol-laden, carcinogenic time bomb.

At the same time, concerns that people in industrialised nations suffered more from constipation, diverticulitis and bowel cancer than those in developing worlds also began to prey on scientists' minds. The answer was no longer fat, it was a different F, the F in the F-Plan. The answer was fibre. In the 1980s, a team of American experts with a sense of humour worked out that the US adult population was carrying a total of 2,297,000,000lb of excess fat. If the calorific energy value of that fat were converted to electricity, there would be enough, they found, to supply the annual residential electricity demands of Boston, Chicago, San Francisco and Washington.

WEIGHTY WORDS

Avoid beans as you would matricide.

Pythagoras

WEIGHTY WORDS

Frugality and a simple table are the mother of health… Now if abstinence is the mother of health, it is plain that eating to repletion is the mother of sickness and ill health, and brings forth diseases… caused by gluttony and satiety… Abstinence [from food], in truth, as it is the mother of health, is also the mother of pleasure; and repletion as it is the source and root of diseases.

John Chrysostom, c. 300 AD

Mummy, must I eat this pie? It's such a particularly nasty bit of the shepherd.

from *Punch*

EIGHTIES MADNESS

In this decade, madness reigned supreme: appetite-suppressing, psychosis-inducing amphetamines were being prescribed left, right and centre; diets were actually managing to kill people; sales of exercise videos were going through the roof. Yet people in both the UK and America were getting inexorably fatter.

The tragic absurdity of the situation reached its peak in 1985. Although the existence of desperate hunger in a world of abundance and plenty is a tale as old as Adam and Eve, the contrast was seldom demonstrated more graphically than it was in this year. While the American government sent $500m to help save the lives of the famine-devastated walking skeletons of Ethiopia, Americans themselves spent 10 times that on diets, pills and exercise programmes, all trying to lose as much weight as the Ethiopians were praying to gain.

DIETING IN THE NINETIES: THE MANY-HEADED HYDRA

This was the decade where the humble dieter began to get nutrition confusion, where no one school of thought dominated and where politics began to invade the dieting arena.

Take the green veg debacle; in January 1992, advice from Canada recommends that we include more cabbage, sprouts and broccoli in our diet to 'protect against the risk of cancer'. Trouble is a US study has found that cabbage administered to rats initiates cancer; that cabbage, but not broccoli, is associated with an increased risk of cervical cancer; but another cabbage – but again, not broccoli – actually protects against colon cancer. In April that same year, President George Bush (the elder) describes broccoli as an unlikeable vegetable. Yet new studies show that it contains sulforaphane, raising enzymes to counter the effects of carcinogens so it really is a super-veg.

Broccoli sales still lag but one American consumer tells the media she is making herself eat it once a week because: 'I just don't want to align myself with that creep, Bush.' The final straw is when broccoli is given the green light on staving off cancer – but in the same study, red-leaf cabbage, beetroot and cauliflower appear to be carcinogenic. Cue a panic in the supermarket as shoppers desperately try to remember which vegetable is good and which is bad, then decide that perhaps it's just safer and easier to go to Pizza Hut.

How about the Bran Balls-Up? Having been solemnly told for two decades that adding wheat bran to the diet could help manage irritable bowel syndrome, a number of placebo-controlled studies come to light in 1994 which fail to identify any benefit at all. Results from a study from St Bart's Hospital in London show that 55% actually felt worse through the addition of a bran supplement, compared to only 10% that felt better. In 1996, research from members of the Imperial Cancer Fund shows that bran could, unbelievably, increase the risk of colorectal cancers. In 1999, the final nail goes into the bran coffin with the news that eating fibre won't prevent cancer of the bowel. So it's F that to the F Plan, then.

Mixed-message advice and research is getting out of hand by the end of the decade. In April 1998, we are told that excessive quantities of vitamin C can be detrimental to health, and could even help trigger serious diseases such as cancer and rheumatoid arthritis. Which is a shame because we've all been packing it away on a regular basis, following previous advice to top up the RDA of 60mg with doses of up to 1,000mg available in the shops, to fight infection and prevent the conversion of nitrates from substances like cigarette smoke and pollution into cancer-causing substances. It's good for Atkins but confusing to people who have been paying any sort of attention to nutrition advice for the previous two decades.

In August 1998, the American Heart Association claims that although eating a low-fat diet can reduce the risk of heart disease, reducing fat to extremely low levels – less than 15% of calorific intake – can increase the presence of triglycerides, the chemical form in which fat is stored in the body. Which means, after all that, that low-fat diets can make you fat.

Then came the news that though the secret of a healthy heart and a functioning brain lay in eating oil-rich fish, those oil-rich fish were often so deeply polluted with mercury and other 'heavy' metals that they might poison you in other ways. It came as no surprise therefore that, in 1995, and in all surveys since, almost half of the responders to an American Dietetic Association (ADA) telephone survey cited that they found news reports on nutrition to be deeply confusing and ultimately unhelpful.

DID YOU NOTICE?

In a moment of surreal hypocrisy, the figure of Betty Crocker, long the symbol of pastry and cake mixes, was altered towards greater slenderness on the packets and boxes being sold from 2000 onwards.

THE AMERICAN PARADOX

In a study published in 1997, it showed that between 1980 and 1990, Americans reduced their calorific intake by 4%, reduced their fat consumption by 11%, and increased their light consumption of 'lite' products (from 19% of the population doing so, to 76%). Yet during that time, the prevalence of obesity increased by 31%.

38cm 39cm 40cm 41cm 42cm 43cm 44cm 45cm 46cm 47cm

THE SWEETEST THING

- 1300 AD: a pound of refined sugar cost a year's pay.
- 1700: Britain imported 20 million pounds of refined sugar per year.
- 1800: the import of refined sugar shot up eightfold to 160 million pounds per year.
- 1850: personal consumption of sugar was up to 20lb of sugar per person per year.
- 1850s: a tax on sugar helped pay for the Crimean War.
- 1874: William Gladstone removed that tax.
- 1900: personal consumption of sugar was up to 72lb per person per year.
- 1980s: we were importing 2.5 million tonnes of sugar – and eating 100lb per every man, woman and child in Britain.

WEIGHTY WORDS

There was a time when I had a 23in waist. I was ten years' old at the time. As I recall, my vital statistics were 23-23-23.

Erma Bombeck

Too much courage has shone among the female kind, and for too many years, for women, under the pretext of loyalty, to break the contract they signed with beauty.

Colette

BRITISH FOOD CONSUMPTION IN THE 2000s

- 1.802 litres of milk (0.914 litres less than in the 1950s)
- 1.9 eggs (1.6 eggs less than in the 1950s)
- 186g cooking fat and oil (143g less than in the 1950s)
- 800g bread (half of that eaten in the 1950s)
- 89g cakes and pastries (100g less than in the 1950s)
- 67g flour (139g less than in the 1950s)
- 567g fruit – 135g citrus fruits, 226g apples and pears, 206g bananas (236g more than in the 1950s; 42g more citrus fruits, 25g more apples and pears, 169g more bananas)
- Income spent on food and non-alcoholic drinks = one sixth (down from one third in the 1950s)

(figures per person per week)

38cm 39cm 40cm 41cm 42cm 43cm 44cm 45cm 46cm 47cm

TODAY'S VITAL STATISTICS

■ We currently spend £133bn a year on food and drink, yet few of us are happy either with our diet or how we look on that diet. According to the Department of Trade and Industry, in the past 50 years we have become, on average, 4kg heavier, 4cm taller and life expectancy has increased by nearly a decade. The average woman, 50 years ago, was 5ft 3in, weighed 118lb (8st 6lb) and had a shoe size 6. Now we are 5ft 4in, weigh 145lb (10st 5lb) and have a shoe size 7.

■ Bosoms have ballooned in size – and it's nothing to do with plastic surgery. Only 10 years ago, the average bra size was 34B. Now, it's at least 36C – and 40% of women wear a D cup or above.

■ The most dramatic change is in our very shape: 50 years ago, the average woman's vital statistics were 33-23-34. Today they are 36-32-38 – a huge change of 9in to our waists. In the next 50 years, it is predicted, women will lose their waists altogether and become barrel-shaped as they increase to 34in. The bad news is that bigger tums will mean more cases of diabetes, high blood pressure and heart disease.

■ Many retailers now admit that a size 12, for example, is rather bigger than 20 years ago, to save customers' blushes. Even as we've grown bigger, our role models have got smaller; a separate study has found that many models and actresses are too thin to be healthy – the majority having 10-15% body fat, compared to the healthy average of 22-26% – and estimated to be thinner than 95% of the rest of the population.

■ The average man is now 5ft 9in with vital statistics of 42-37-40, weighing 174lb (12st 6lb) – taller and fatter than before.

LAST FEW DECADES

It would seem that we eat less than we did in the 1950s and spend less but are getting inexorably fatter. In fact, what this doesn't take into account are the figures for food eaten outside the home, which have increased exponentially since the 1950s.

One thing emerging from the confusing murk of the last few decades is that there is plenty to pick and choose from in our ancestors' diets, should we want to. Here are a few suggestions:

1. Use the Romans' way with vegetables, cooked nicely spiced fish dishes and lack of sugar, manufactured fats or processed food. Just try not to join them on the tickle-throat-with-feather idea.

2. The medieval diet depended on spit-roasting quality meat and using fresh herbs to liven up vegetables and omelettes, but steer clear of the sweet-toothed stuff.

3. From the Victorians, fresh shellfish is an obvious low-fat choice while the broths and consommés are full of nutrients and minerals, but avoid their vegetables, which usually had the nutrients cooked out of them.

4. From wartime rationing, reduce your fatty meat intake, keep saturated fats low, ban salt and sugar and be as imaginative as they were with pulses and beans.

Bon appetit!

WEIGHTY WORDS

My mother's wartime menu consisted of two choices: take it or leave it.

Buddy Hackett

CULTURAL DIFFERENCES

For some reason, as yet unexplained, a trip to Europe always seems to help with weight reduction. It may be something in the soil... the best results seem to be achieved in Mediterranean countries: Spain, Greece, Italy, the South of France.

Dr Robert Atkins, writer of *Dr Atkins New Diet Revolution*, puzzling over the Mediterranean diet in 1972

Even as little as a hundred years ago, cultural differences in diet and different approaches to weight loss would have filled the pages of a book all on its own. Now, as those differences blur and nations become more 'developed' in the Western sense, so too do the truisms of national diet.

The World Health Organisation claims that 60% of deaths around the world are 'clearly related' to changing dietary patterns and the increased consumption of fatty, salty and sugary foods. On the other hand, we are also spreading our cultural prejudices about fat, body image and beauty into communities that used to prize fat and fat women in particular.

We say, let's chuck all the cultural ideas, the tips, the hang-ups into a big pot and stir up a delicious brew that we might actually want to live off and digest. But that would get us obsessing about food again and isn't that what got us into this trouble in the first place?

REVENGE OF THE PEASANTS

The European revolutions may be a distant memory for both Europe and America, but it is a social legacy that dictates what we consider to be the norm in our diet. During the Age of Enlightenment of the seventeenth and eighteenth centuries, the emerging middle classes in Western Europe had less fear of disease, plague and famine than before and the food supply was more assured. Haute cuisine – fancy food based on meat, dairy produce, refined sugar, processed flour – was developed by the middle classes as one way of boasting about their new security and riches. Today, such richness of food is still considered to be the 'ideal', the desirable, the 'treat' in Britain, the USA, France and most other Western European countries. But why do we still hold as a treat a way of eating that is unnatural, unbalanced and artificially prepared?

'Peasant' food, be it fresh Mediterranean pasta or Asian curries, is now as widely eaten in Britain as other forms of cuisine yet 'fine dining' falls back on the artificiality of haute cuisine, and the likes of brown rice, lentils and wholewheat pasta still has more than a whiff of the hippie about it. Until we break such social conventions, diets will always be diets, not lifestyles, and Britons will always be struggling.

DID YOU KNOW?

In the Highlands of Scotland a midwife traditionally gave a newborn baby a small spoonful of earth and a tot of whisky as its first meal.

FAT IS A CLASSIST ISSUE

Forget the cultural differences; in this century as in the last, as journalist Polly Toynbee said, 'This obesity debate is full of humbug and denial. Fat is a class issue, but few like to admit that most of the seriously obese are poor.' The country is divided between those who make their own chicken stock from organic bones and those who just nuke chicken nuggets in the microwave, between £9 loaves of seed bread and sliced white for 55p. America has by far the most unequal society and by far the fattest – Britain and Australia come next. The narrower the status and income gap between high- and low-born, the narrower the waistbands. But can we also blame the government? Scandinavian countries have successfully changed both diets and attitudes throughout society with various measures like tough labelling laws, a ban on adverts for junk food, promoting cycle routes in cities and a thorough overhaul of education policies on school food and sport. Now the British government have finally banned fizzy drinks and junk food in vending machines in schools. Could this be the turning of the tide?

THE FRENCH PARADOX

How can the French, with their partiality for more than a drop of wine and their great lust for bread, cheese and coffee, maintain both their figures and their happily beating hearts well into a golden old age? Their national cuisine is known for its rich, creamy sauces, heroic carnivorism, washed down by wine, cigarettes and precious little exercise. Yet they have the lowest heart attack rates in Europe – and only 7% of the French are obese, compared to 22% of Americans.

According to one French scientist, Serge Renaud, the answer is simple: red wine. In 1991, he demonstrated that red wine could reduce the risk of coronary disease by at least 40%. Moderate and regular consumption of red wine, he said, interrupts the growth of all micro-organisms and maintains good levels of cholesterol while increasing the flexibility and diameter of individual arteries. But the key is clearly in one magic word, a word that we in the UK and especially our fat friends in the USA, have a major problem in recognising and doing anything about: moderation.

It took a team of scientists from the University of Pennsylvania to state what we all knew in our hearts: the French may have all this wicked food, but they don't eat very much of it. It's all about portion control, that other little-understood concept on these shores and across the Atlantic. Anyone ordering a meal in a restaurant in Philadelphia will get a much bigger portion than someone ordering the same meal in Paris. The difference can be by as much as a quarter, unless you eat in a Chinese restaurant in Philly, which will serve a staggering 72% more than their counterparts in France.

WEIGHTY WORDS

Don't worry, I move very well – I haven't crushed a little girl in, oh, days.

Patricia Lehigh, 30+ stone member of NAAFA, America's National Association to Advance Fat Acceptance

Inhabitants of underdeveloped nations and victims of natural disasters are the only people who have ever been happy to see soybeans.

Fran Lebowitz

Tofu is actually enjoyed as a food in parts of Asia.

Vic Reeves

FRENCH WOMEN DON'T GET FAT

This is actually now the name of a book by a slim, high-powered and well-groomed French woman, Mireille Giuliano, who lives in New York. French women don't get fat, she says, not for genetic reasons, but cultural ones. It's because they don't diet, they don't calorie count, they don't go to the gym, they don't anxiously step onto the scales every morning or regard any food as 'bad'. They simply come up with a lifelong stratagem for keeping slim – and then just don't eat very much, and eat it slowly, sitting down at a table. With napkins. Do you hate her yet?

Her suggestion for her fellow New Yorkers is to, well, become French, but then she spoils even that by saying there are some things – like tying a scarf – that only Frenchwomen know how to do. What she gives away only in unguarded asides – like the anecdote of her father telling her she looked like a sack of potatoes – is the less palatable cultural difference: that fatness in France is regarded with horror and disdain and that those slim, chic Frenchwomen we are meant to admire actually just have an unhealthy obsession with being thin.

WEIGHTY WORDS

You British, I think, are losing the relationship with food, of admiring the fact that your body needs good food for the body and the spirit. When you lose contact with ingredients, you're reduced to a dependency.

Antonio Carluccio, chef

Peckish is not the word. I feel like a homeless tapeworm.

PG Wodehouse

GALLIC CHARM

Pick up a tub of French body lotion and it might make for disturbing reading for the vast majority of women who have stretch marks. Never one to suffer fat fools gladly, stretch marks, in French, are called *marques disgracieuses* which seems to translate into something suspiciously like 'marks of disgrace'. No, no, speak your mind, Mr French Cosmetician, because you can bet your last euro, it was a man who came up with that phrase…

MAMMA MIA

Italian children are now the fattest in Europe, according to the World Health Organisation, so what's happened? Two things: American fast food has, as it has all over the globe, made huge inroads in Italy, while the pressures of modern living have induced an almost sedentary lifestyle. 'There is something wrong with the way we live,' muses chef Antonio Carluccio. 'Generally, all of Italy now suffers from American culture shock – through the media and the fast-food corporations. Italians have one child, and that child is idle, never goes out to play. Parents are lazy, they don't cook, they just go to the pizzeria... you can't be healthy living like that.'

Gone, say some, are the days when an Italian housewife simply went to the market to see what was fresh. Others blame the Americanisation of Italian food – smothering pasta in rich, creamy sauces where before there was the merest slick of a ragu or tomato-based sauce; bread being served with butter or dunked in olive oil; spaghetti bolognese delivered in quantities that would have fed an entire Italian family a few decades ago, and with garlic bread on the side. Rose Gray of London's River Café, which promotes the simplest, freshest Italian food, is optimistic that all is not lost in Italy. 'They haven't quite sunk into the weekly supermarket shop; if you watch people shopping, you can see that they still care like mad.'

OVERWEIGHT AND OVER THERE

One culture that has an impressive love-hate relationship with fat, the nutrient, is the American culture. Even with all the advances in food nutrition and research, most of which took place in the US, the American diet still derives 60% of its calories from two nutrients: sugar and fat. The average American eats 135lb of fat per year – that translates to one tonne every 15 years.

A recent Starbucks product – the Double Chocolate Chip Frappuccino Blended Crème – won the 'Food Porn of the Month Award' from the Centre for Science in the Public Interest (CSPI). It didn't win for the best hard-core food ad (which featured a muscly man provocatively licking off frothy curls from the top), but for food products that the CSPI considers to be impressively unhealthy. A 20oz 'venti' contains 600 calories and 16g of fat. Oh, and not a whisper of coffee, should you be fooled by the name at all... the CSPI, instead, calls them 'fattuccinos'.

Women's food intake in the US has increased three times as much as men's, now 22% more over the last 30 years, yet over half profess to be on a diet at any given time – and to despise fat. Even the introduction of low-fat foods – 5,000 lower fat versions of foods between 1995-1997 alone – caused only a short-lived decline in total fat intake, either because people didn't like the taste of the low-fat products or because they added fat to their low-fat item to improve the taste (such as adding a cream swirl to a skimmed milk latte).

WEIGHTY WORDS

The German sausage looked like a cross-section through a dead dachshund.

Clive James

Tomato and oregano make it Italian, wine and tarragon make it French, sour cream makes it Russian, lemon and cinnamon make it Greek, soy sauce makes it Chinese, garlic makes it GOOD!

Alice May Brock

GETTING SOME PERSPECTIVE

Hunger is considered an entirely normal state of affairs among the Hausa of Niger so dieting isn't exactly top of the agenda; abnormality comes when there is an inability to control their states of hunger. In the Sudan, the term for eating stands for a number of pleasures such as having money, power or sex. Likewise the vocabulary for hunger stands for almost all types of suffering – 'famine' is not just a single term but rather famines are given distinct names to reflect the intensity of deprivation. For a mild famine, the names indicate shortage of grain; for more serious, the names reflect the wild foods consumed when all else is gone; for the worst, the vocabulary embraces the threat of irrevocable destitution – in Sudan, this is greater than the threat of death.

38cm | 39cm | 40cm | 41cm | 42cm | 43cm | 44cm | 45cm | 46cm | 47cm

FOREIGN FOOD PRODUCTS AS APPETITE SUPRESSANTS

- Sor Bits (Danish mints)
- Nora Knackers (Norwegian biscuits)
- Mukki (Italian yoghurt)
- Plopp (Swedish toffee bar)
- Bum (Turkish biscuits)
- Donkee Basterd Suker (Dutch sugar)
- Bimbo Bread (South America)
- Craps Chocolate (France)
- Homo-Milk (Canada)

DIETING TO BE FAT

Among the desert Arabs of Niger, a country that borders Nigeria in the south and Algeria in the north, women strive to be as fat as possible, with girls even being force-fed to achieve this ideal. Even in early childhood, under the close watch of a female relative, girls begin ingesting large quantities of milk and porridge every day, thereafter maintaining the weight gain by stuffing themselves with a kind of greasy couscous.

There is an element of 'prosperity' in this aspiration – the successfully fat women spend as much time as possible lying down, getting servants to do all household tasks – but there is also an aesthetic appreciation of the fat state. Western ideals – as demonstrated by girls in magazines – are met with scornful derision and unflattering comparisons to scrawny cows. Niger Arabs instead covet smooth chests, with no hint of collarbones and a long fleshy neck on which to display necklaces. When they walk, they walk as slowly as they can, swaying their buttocks from side to side to emphasise the attractive size of their charms. So important are big buttocks to femininity in Niger that the simple dolls girls make out of clay often have no arms or legs, but have clearly sculpted buttocks.

Stretch marks are sung about glowingly in a love song as a 'waist lined with stripes' and all women aspire to get them not only on the stomachs and hips but on their legs and arms as well. But things are changing. Having performed poorly before, in the 2001 Miss World beauty contest, Nigeria entered a tall, svelte girl whose skinny appearance appealed to few in Nigeria itself. She won, and thereafter the younger women have begun to see Western ideals as an alternative target.

A MINUTE
ON THE LIPS...
Gerkin

THE 1999 EXPERIMENT

In 1999, the American Heart Association (AHA) conducted an infamous experiment to measure the different impacts on heart disease patients of the Mediterranean diet. Some patients were given olive oil as the main fat, with staples of fresh fruit, fresh vegetables, lightly cooked fish and wine, while others had the AHA diet, which recommended cutting out saturated fats such as egg yolks, whole milk dairy products, cheese and fatty meats. Those on the Mediterranean diet showed dramatic improvements after six weeks. Those on the AHA diet showed little or no improvement – some even died, leading to the abrupt ending of the experiment – and their risk of heart failure, heart attack, embolism and cardiac deficiency was 75% higher than the happy Mediterranean eaters.

RAMADAN: THE THIRD PILLAR OF WISDOM

In Islam, fasting is not a trendy diet but a once-a-year reality during Ramadan. Known also as 'sawm', the period of fasting represents the third pillar of wisdom and was encouraged by the Prophet during the month of Ramadan, which is the ninth lunar month in the Muslim calendar.

Abstinence from food is not a penance as it is in the Christian faith, but the means, according to the Koran, to become more conscious of Allah. Fasting occurs for able-bodied Muslims between sunrise and sunset of every day during the month. Menstruating, pregnant and nursing women, the sick and very young children are not required to fast, although there is an obligation to make up days missed later or to substitute with acts of charity. The end of Ramadan is celebrated with the Eid al-Fitr, the Feast of the Breaking Fast, which lasts for three days.

CULTURAL CONTRADICTIONS

The Inuit people of Alaska and Canada, while not of supermodel proportions, enjoy a very low incidence of heart disease and extremely good health, yet they have a diet extremely high in saturated fats. The seal, whale blubber, salmon and swordfish they live on, however, are also packed with healthy, omega-3, polyunsaturated 'good' fats from all the plankton and algae consumed at sea. This, in conjunction with the 15% higher resting metabolic rates needed to survive the freezing cold, counteracts the 'bad' fats and leaves them with an insulating layer of fat that may not win modelling contracts, but is super-healthy.

Meanwhile, in Finland during the 1960s, Finnish lumberjacks exercised vigorously every day and were extremely lean and muscular, yet suffered extraordinarily high rates of heart disease. By 1971, Finland had the highest death rate in the world from heart disease. The anomaly was traced to the lumberjacks' habit of eating nearly 5,000 calories a day, most of which was in the form of saturated fats – pork and dairy products – to which they added piles of salt; they also indulged in excessive smoking and pooh-poohed the need for fruit and vegetables. The government encouraged the use of vegetable oil in place of lard, promoted fresh fruit and veg tirelessly and lobbied against salt. In 1997, the heart disease rates had halved, proving both that weight and health do not necessarily go hand in hand, but also that any culture can change, if the public and private will is there.

Israelis eat much less fat than Americans (33% of their calories, versus nearly 44%) but they have higher rates of heart disease, obesity, diabetes and cancer. They also have one of the highest ratios of 'good' to 'bad' fats in the world; 8% better than America and 10% higher than Europe, consuming as they do large amounts of soybean, safflower, sunflower and corn oil – all rich in omega-6 fats

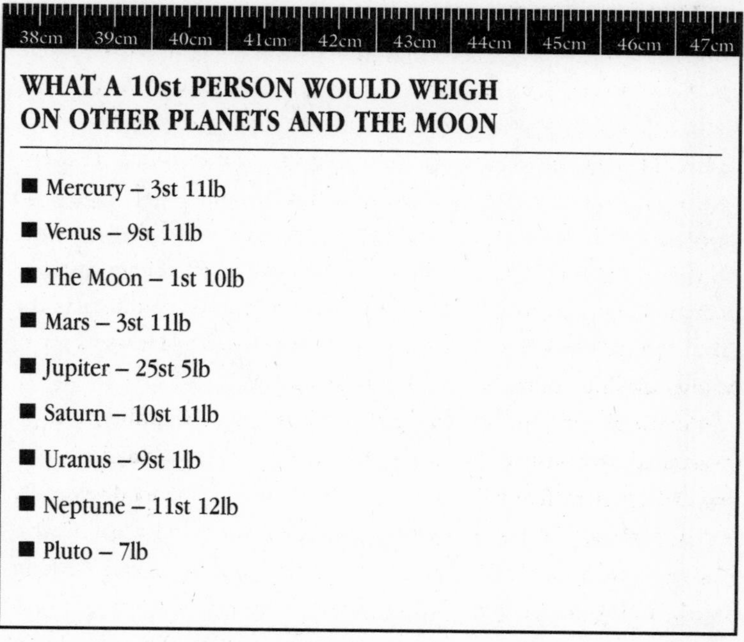

WHAT A 10st PERSON WOULD WEIGH ON OTHER PLANETS AND THE MOON

- Mercury – 3st 11lb
- Venus – 9st 11lb
- The Moon – 1st 10lb
- Mars – 3st 11lb
- Jupiter – 25st 5lb
- Saturn – 10st 11lb
- Uranus – 9st 1lb
- Neptune – 11st 12lb
- Pluto – 7lb

essential for good health. Why? Possibly this falls into the 'too much of a good thing' pigeonhole: they're eating good fats, but in high doses, polyunsaturated fats can lead to insulin resistance, thrombosis, coronary disease and cancer. Meanwhile, the Arab Israelis are a much healthier lot – they cook with olive oil.

HAVING THE FAMILY FOR DINNER

In some Aboriginal tribes, careful rules governed who could eat whom when it came to handing out the slices of flesh from a corpse before it was buried. A man could eat his sister's husband and his brother's wife, but not his children. A child could not eat his or her father, while a mother was able to eat her children and vice versa.

HEALTHY IS AS HEALTHY DOES

Around the world, there are communities where people live lean and live long. Okinawa Archipelago, Japan, is home to the world's longest-living people: there are 34 centenarians per 100,000 compared to five per 100,000 in the UK. They also have the lowest global levels of heart disease and strokes, and the highest incidence of recovery from the few cancers that beset them. Diet is based on six daily servings of sweet potatoes, leafy greens and wholegrains, supplemented with fish, rice, pork and soya products, for an average daily calorie count of 1,500. Green tea is the beverage of choice. Okinawans are fishermen or farmers and work outdoors even into their 80s and meditate regularly. Turning Japanese, I think it's time to be turning Japanese, I really think so, just to paraphrase the only Japanese-themed song we know.

The inhabitants of Simi Island, situated off the Turkish coast in Greece, regularly live into their 90s on the purest version of the famously healthy Mediterranean diet: olive oil, fish, tomato sauces, raw or lightly cooked veg, salads and little meat. Most Simiots eat double the recommended five-a-day portions of fruit and vegetables, washed down at most meals by moderate amounts of wine (hurrah!) and afterwards by sage tea in preference to coffee. Some experts believe that Mediterranean men's ability to express their feelings may lower stress – and women to maintain their body image and, therefore, their weight.

Semitropical Bama, in south-west China, is cut off by mountains on all sides, and is still resistant to the waves of fast food and soft drinks swamping the rest of the nation. Robust immune systems and a low incidence of heart disease and cancer are testament to the low-calorie, low-fat, low-salt diet. Brown rice (unusually in China), tomatoes, peppers, leafy greens and a compendium of fresh and dried herbs enable them to have plenty of aerobic activity for moving up and down the mountains. Singing contests – popular for all ages – are held to keep brains alert, stress relieved and the immune system boosted.

Described as the 'happy land of just enough' and the inspiration of the mythical Shangri-la, in the Hunza Valley, Pakistan, cancer rates there are at zero and digestive disorders associated with Western diets simply do not exist. Hunzukuts eat around 1,900 calories a day but think nothing of walking 60 miles (96km) to the nearest town, ramming in apricots as they go (between 50-100 in a day, with apricot-eating competitions being regularly held) to supplement their diet of spinach, wholewheat chapatti bread, beans, pulses and root vegetables.

38cm 39cm 40cm 41cm 42cm 43cm 44cm 45cm 46cm 47cm

NO THANKS, I'M WATCHING MY WEIGHT – 10 DISHES FROM AROUND THE WORLD

1. Calf Udder Croquettes (France)
2. Pig's Organs in Blood Sauce (Philippines)
3. Parrot Pie (actually 12 budgies) (Australia)
4. Stewed Cane Rat (Ghana)
5. Calf's Lung and Heart in Cocktail Sauce (Hungary)
6. Fox Tongues (Japan)
7. Cajun Squirrel Ravioli (USA)
8. Lambs' Tails and Honey (Morocco)
9. Sun-dried Maggots (China)
10. Coconut-Cream-marinated Dog (Indonesia)

MOTHER TONGUE

There's nothing so culturally divisive as the subject of how to treat a woman's diet in pregnancy. In France, pregnant women are discouraged from putting on weight. One Englishwoman said: 'I had my baby in Paris. My obstetrician told me to drink a glass of champagne a day to help me remain calm – and didn't warn me off soft cheeses like Camembert or Brie – but was very strict about monitoring my weight.'

The soft cheese debate rages around listeria, present in mould-ripened cheeses like Camembert or Brie, blue cheese or unpasteurised soft goats' and sheep's cheese. But while the French roundly ignore such risks, other cultures go overboard: many English and American mums-to-be give cream cheese and even fromage frais a miss, both of which are good sources of calcium and protein and have no exposure to listeria whatsoever.

In Italy, mothers-to-be are encouraged to drink espressos galore, tuck into prosciutto and omelettes, all of which American moms are horrified by because of the imagined health risks in meats that are cured rather than cooked, the poisons of caffeine and the potential salmonella risk of partially cooked eggs.

In America and New Zealand, drinking any amount of alcohol during pregnancy is frowned upon – yet in France, many women drink as normal during pregnancy. It's not generally that much – that darned French moderation thing again – but woe betide the pregnant mother who tucks into a similarly moderate glass of wine in the US.

Fiona Ford, a research dietitian, says there is no actual proof that eight to 10 units a week (a glass of champagne a day) has any harm but puts in the caveat that 'nobody can say exactly what a safe amount of alcohol is, as experts are loath to run the necessary tests on pregnant women.'

After childbirth, cultural differences really kick in – breastfeeding, regarded as *the* weight-loss tip for new mothers in the UK, is generally disdained by French women, who, like most celebrities, just crack right on into the weight-loss programme. This regime is also helped out by the state which pays for 10 physiotherapist sessions to 're-educate' your pelvic floor (dating back to post-World War I when, because there were so few men-folk, the nation decided French married women needed to get back into shape quickly for more breeding) and a further 10 sessions to flatten your stomach.

WEIGHTY WORDS

There's a new Chinese diet. Order all the food you want but only use one chopstick.

Bob Monkhouse

Dried fish is like a staple food in Iceland. It varies in roughness. The tougher kind tastes like toenails, and the softer kind like the skin off the soles of one's feet.

WH Auden

I asked the sales assistant in the clothes store if she had anything to make me look thinner, and she said, 'How about a week in Ethiopia?'

Roseanne Barr

You don't eat Mexican food – you just rent it.

Alexei Sayle

A woman can never be too rich or too thin.

The Duchess of Windsor

WHY ANIMALS DON'T HAVE EATING DISORDERS

■ Horses, rabbits and rats can't vomit – no chance of bulimia for them.

■ It takes a sloth up to six days to digest the food it eats – so can we assume it's got a high-GI diet?

■ The South American anteater eats around 30,000 ants a day – now that's snacking.

■ The stomach of a hippopotamus is 10ft long – quite a contender for gastric bypass surgery, we say.

■ An elephant can eat a tonne of grass a day – on the Hay Diet, then?

■ Cats can't taste sweet food – so chocolate is wasted on them.

■ Frogs and toads push food down into their stomach with the back of their eyeballs – so it's lucky their eyes aren't too big for their stomachs.

■ Pet parrots can eat most of the food humans eat, apart from chocolate and avocado which are highly toxic to them – oh, if only we had that disincentive.

■ Tarantulas can go for up to two years without eating – so who are we to complain about a few hours' fasting?

■ Whales increase their weight 30 *billion* times in their first two years, but can swim for three months without eating – so we'd like to see which diet Gillian McKeith would put them on.

■ Five piranha fish could chew a horse and rider up in seven minutes – which we guess puts them on a high-protein diet?

■ The only food cockroaches won't eat is cucumber – which rules out a Greek salad for them.

■ Some ribbon worms will eat bits of themselves if they can't find any food – which puts the Liz Hurley hunger diet into perspective.

■ Given sufficient amounts of chocolate, pigs can master video game skills – we knew there was a rationale to chocolate.

THE MARRYING KIND

In our increasingly besieged marriage culture, those who eat and stay together, although they eat more, in the long term find that marriage makes women slimmer. Having children does not help the initial battle of the average 6-8lb bulge (women face an average 7% increased risk of obesity per child born, and men, who cannot blame pregnancy but are clearly just jumping on the bandwagon, risk a 4% increased tendency to obesity) but, over time, a married woman's weight stays the same. On the other hand, 70.6% of American husbands were overweight or obese (compared to 65.1% of all US men) but were more likely to eat healthily, having more vegetables, lean poultry and with less sugary drinks than their single equivalents. Both men and women were also more physically active if they were in a relationship. Women who were single, widowed, divorced or unhappily married gained weight, despite most professing to worrying about their weight and dieting almost constantly.

FATTY BOOM-BOOM

One thing that spans cultures is the love of fat as a flavour. Fatty foods, as culinary historians note, are often prized as specialities due to their satisfying taste. Think of French foie gras (goose liver pâté), English Stilton cheese, Italian pancetta, Buffalo chicken wings, Spanish ham or even Southern fried chicken – all animal fats, saturated, unhealthy, delicious. Few cultures these days, however, go as brazenly far as the Italians do in their love of *lardo*, which means, simply, lard. Slimy, white slices of fat, served up in curls, to be eaten with fresh toast and pepper. Or in *minestra di lard* – lard soup – which consists of lard, a garlic clove, half a cabbage, rice and some grana or hard cheese like Parmesan, which goes down a storm, especially in Italy's north-east regions. If it weren't for the fact that they eat carbohydrates as well, you could almost think they were on the Atkins Diet…

SNACK ATTACK

Britain is now the snack capital of Europe, according to market analysts Datamonitor, where one meal in five is simply a grazing buffet. In Britain, 22% of us eat on the go compared to just 16% in France and 15% in Holland. When our Swedish or Dutch friends go on the snack attack, they are as likely to choose fruit and nuts to satisfy their urges (44% and 43% of the time) – two out of three times, we plump for crisps, chocolate and fast food.

We can take the charitable view which is that it's because we work harder, have lost the culture of the lunch hour and are dependent on a high street stuffed to the gills with junk food, but the conclusion is inescapable: changing work patterns, rising commute times and the breakdown of regular mealtimes mean we are spending more time eating and drinking either on the move, or working on the job. Even when we dump the junk and go posh on our snacks, it's still fattening stuff; instead of a simple apple, our snack is as likely to be some Japanese rice crackers or a blueberry muffin. And it's set to get worse. By 2007, an estimated 29% of eating and drinking will be on the move.

So lobby your boss for a decent lunch hour, barrack your local shops for some decent, healthy fare and rediscover the joys of eating while sitting at a table, conversing. It's better for you – eating food more slowly and with pauses for conversation means you chew more and digest more easily.

AVOCADO

We know that the avocado is the world's most nutritious fruit, yet we're confused as to whether its high fat content makes it friend or foe. There's no such ambivalence in Latin America: in Chile, Colombia and Brazil, the avocado is often wrapped and given as a wedding present to the bride. Well, it beats getting another toaster.

HEAVYWEIGHTS OF THE WEIGHT-LOSS WORLD

My advice to you is... if you're a fat and ugly girl, you should not buy these DVDs 'cos you haven't got a chance of looking like these three Cheshire kittens

Chris Moyles, talking to his listeners on Radio 1, while interviewing Jodi Albert, Ali Bastian and Sarah Dunn about their *Hollyoaks Dance Workout* DVD

Some of them are evangelists, with a frightening zeal for the message they have to spread; some of them are charlatans, only a couple of steps on from nineteenth-century 'Dr Caractacus Winklebaum & His Incredible Shrinking Potions' quacks. Some of them are medical professionals, some of them are soap stars. Some of them are naturally fit and skinny; and some used to be fat and now want us to share in their zeal for what got them thin.

All of them are on a mission: to turn us lard-buckets into lean, mean, dieting machines who think nothing of jogging five miles (8km) before our porridge oats – and, more importantly, think nothing of spending another £15 on an exercise video to fit in before our kidney bean casserole that night.

They are the food gurus, the personal trainers, the heavyweights of the workout world, and we have been out with our sheepdogs to round them up on these pages. Is Jane Fonda still going for the burn? Is Rosemary Conley more 'chicken thigh' than 'hip and thigh' these days? What did happen to Dr Atkins? And what is the big deal about exercise anyway?

HEALTH EXPERTS AND HOW THEY DIED

When Robert Atkins died after a fall on an icy pavement in April 2003, at the very peak of Atkins Diet mania, the world was shocked. Here was one of the first billionaires of the dieting age and he slips to his death on an icy pavement? How are the mighty fallen, we all said. Then the coroner's report, in which it was revealed that Atkins weighed 258lb (18st 6lb), started to cause consternation. 258lb? But that's technically obese, said commentators.

Soon Atkins critics were dancing on his grave. He was fat! they crowed. Dr Atkins, Dr Fatkins! The man who insisted the bad breath, constipation and aches and pains were mere side effects of a pain-free, pleasurable regime that turned the notion of dieting on its head actually had the temerity to be a porker! All those who had warned for years that his diet was a recipe for heart disease, seized on the handwritten notes, 'M I' in the medical report that suggested 'myocardial infarction' as evidence that he had a history of congestive heart problems.

In vain did his family insist that he had put on more than 56lb (4st) in the eight days he lay in hospital before his death: fluid retention from the coma, they said. That is the weight of an eight-year-old child – that's a lot of water, answered the critics and the damage was done. The man who, as an overweight 32-year-old, had a 'Eureka!' moment in 1963 when he stumbled across the fat-causing effects of carbohydrates in low-fat foods, had, when he died, dragged down the empire he had spent 30 years building up. Suddenly the door was open for the diet's many critics to shout out and to shout out loud. By July 2005, less than two years' later, the diet company that had ruled the world had gone bankrupt, with debts of nearly $300m. From fat profits to slim pickings, it was an appropriately dramatic fall from grace for a man who had so dramatically – if too radically – rewritten the conventions of dieting.

Emile Coué (1857-1926) Trained as a pharmacist, Coué became interested in hypnotism and developed a health treatment based on auto-suggestion. He told his patients – by World War I, an estimated 40,000 a year – that their health would improve dramatically if, morning and evening, they repeated faithfully the now famous – and much misquoted – mantra: 'Every day and in every way, I am becoming better and better.' Sadly the mantra could not stave off Coué's own downfall: after one of his lecture tours he returned home, complained of exhaustion and soon after died of heart failure.

JI Rodale (1889-1971) Newspaper and magazine baron Rodale was at the height of his fame when he appeared on *The Dick Cavett Show* in 1971 to talk about his belief in organic food supplemented by natural vitamins. After describing the dangers of milk, wheat and sugar, Rodale proceeded to say: 'I'm so healthy that I expect to live on and on and on.' Shortly, after the conclusion of the interview, Rodale slumped in his chair, the victim of a fatal heart attack.

Linus Pauling (1901-1994) The only person to win two unshared Nobel Prizes (for Chemistry and Peace), Pauling wrote a book arguing that large doses of vitamin C could cure the common cold. Over the years he expanded on his claims, declaring that vitamin C extended a person's life by decades and would ward off cancer and heart disease. Pauling himself took 18,000mg of vitamin C a day (the RDA for adults is 60mg) but died of prostate cancer in 1994.

Adelle Davis (1904-1974) 'You are what you eat,' declared Davis, the well-known American nutritionist, who said that disease could be staved off with a natural diet rich in fresh fruits, vegetables and large doses of vitamins. When she was diagnosed as having bone cancer at the age of 69, her first reaction was disbelief. 'I thought cancer was for people who drink soft drinks, who eat white bread, who eat refined sugar and so on,' she said. She died a year later.

Irwin Stillman (1910-1975) On a promise of 'eat fat, lose fat', Dr Irwin Stillman published the *Quick Weight Loss Diet* in 1967, a forerunner of Atkins, which also promised ketosis and magical weight loss on a high-fat, high-protein, low-carb diet. 'If you're 10% overweight,' Stillman said, 'you'll lose seven years of living. In effect you will have committed suicide at the age of 63.' Some 20 million people bought into it but Stillman proved to be his own worst propaganda when he dropped dead of a heart attack only seven years later.

Herman Tarnower (1910-1980) The Scarsdale Diet millionaire had been in a relationship with headmistress Jean Harris for 14 years. When womaniser Dr Tarnower's attentions strayed, Harris – who had also run out of the amphetamine Desoxyn that he regularly prescribed for her to suppress her appetite on his diet regime – lost control. Saying later that she had planned suicide but needed to see him one last time, Harris took a gun and drove for five hours until she reached Dr Tarnower's house. When she arrived they had a furious argument, the gun went off and Tarnower was killed.

Jim Fixx (1932-1984) Writing from personal experience, Fixx trumpeted the health benefits of running. After starting to jog at age 35, he quit smoking and shed 50lb (3st 8lb). Yet at age 52, Fixx collapsed while running on a tree-shaded road in Vermont. He was found lying beside the road, dead of a heart attack.

Stuart M Berger (1953-1994) The enormously tall Berger successfully reduced his weight from 420lb (30st) to 210lb (15st), then described his techniques in such bestsellers as *The Southampton Diet* (1984) and *Dr Berger's Immune Power Diet* (1986). He died in his New York apartment from a heart attack brought on by cocaine abuse and obesity: at his death he weighed 364lb (26st).

When feeling sad, men are $1\frac{1}{2}$ times more likely to jog or pump iron than women, who are 22 times more likely than men to "pig out on chocolate."

THE DEAD CAT AND THE DOCTOR

When *Guardian* journalist Ben Goldacre's dead cat managed to qualify for the same 'professional membership' from the American Association of Nutritional Consultants as Dr Gillian McKeith, we all wondered just how qualified this 'nutritional expert' was to say: 'You Are What You Eat'. Details, details, according to Dr McKeith. 'My education is stellar. I've been on so many courses. I've had thousands of patients over the years who would rave about me.' Not quite the same as a professional qualification, Gillian, but never mind.

Ever since she burst onto our TV screens on BBC's *Good Morning* and then with her own series in 2003, this half-pint powerhouse has been at the forefront of the GI revolution – poking around in poo, taking chubby celebrities in hand and trying to get us all enthused about foodstuffs with kerrrazy names like quinoa, tempeh, aduki, carob, millet and miso. She has the usual road-to-Damascus story of her conversion from a grim life of migraines, chronic fatigue, eating junk and painful scoliosis to a healthy-eating life of macrobiotic miracles and is now, in her late 40s, suitably thin, perky and clear-eyed. Born in Scotland, with a stint at Edinburgh University, she is vague when it comes to the large proportion of her life that she spent in America: a distance-learning degree here, a bankrupted health-food chain there, but has eloquent conviction in spades.

When she was 12, she says, she had a vision: she was on stage, talking to hundreds of people. The messianic zeal is undoubted. The trouble is, she's just so annoying. Leaving aside the sketchy CV – and admitting that her TV series is a hit and the accompanying books are massive bestsellers – much of what McKeith says is a bit dodgy. Floating stools that will not flush show a liver imbalance? Not according to expert, qualified dietitians – 'It is impossible to diagnose medical conditions from looking at a normal brown stool, floating or not.' A 'living food' powder that contains all the goodness and enzymes of raw food? One nutritional professor challenged her to prove it, offering her £1,000, but was not surprised when she refused. And then there's the tongue thing. Gillian McKeith has a thing about tongues – 'Oh, I love tongue analysis. And I'm really good at it' – but dietitians say it's impossible to pick up everything that she 'sees' just by looking at someone's tongue. Is McKeith a quack or is she just the victim of professional jealousy? We'll let you decide.

38cm 39cm 40cm 41cm 42cm 43cm 44cm 45cm 46cm 47cm

THROUGH THE LOOKING GLASS: THE TRUTH BEHIND THE FITNESS INDUSTRY

- A quarter of people who get exercise equipment to fight post-Christmas flab will use it only twice. The equipment will then either be put away 'for a rainy day', sold on eBay or, mostly, used as a clothes-hanging device.

- A tenth of exercise machines and fitness videos won't even make it out of their boxes: pollsters for St Ivel's Gold estimated there are over two million get-fit videos gathering dust, over one million exercise bikes lying idle and nearly one and a half million sets of dumbbells out of action.

- About 35% of Brits own fitness gear – spending £238m a year on it, but 29% of women and 20% of men admit that it is never used.

- A quarter of us are gym members – but nearly half have not been there for at least a month. Of those questioned, 6% hate every minute they spend at a fitness centre, but have the willpower to go regularly, while a tenth of people who do go would consider themselves exercise addicts.

- Pet hates in the gym? 11% hate men who insist on showing off their muscles; 17% grumble about queuing for weights machines and 13% just can't stand the sheer boredom of it all.

WEIGHTY WORDS

Now some women fantasise nightly
Of erotic adventures and steam.
But without sounding drab, all I want to grab
Is a bucket or two of ice-cream.

Pam Ayres

The omelette on this diet was so light we had to lay our knives across it and even then it struggled.

Margaret Halsey

WORKOUT WOES

The Royal Society for the Prevention of Accidents (RSPA) has put the boot in to home workouts and exercise videos/DVDs. After figures revealed that 14,000 exercisers are treated in hospital each year after working out at home, the RSPA said most injuries happened because of over-exertion or exercisers hitting others with flailing arms, hitting walls or poking family members in the eye. Other accidents included falling off steps, skiing machines or treadmills.

Of those who watched exercise DVDs, many set themselves up for injury by fast-forwarding sections that offered safety advice or warm-up instructions and then by struggling to keep up with the instructor on screen. 'It's important people do follow advice,' said a society spokesman, 'and, if they see something beyond their capabilities, that they don't just assume it's safe for them to copy it because it's on the video.' So turn off the grinning little popstrel doing the splits on the telly and have a nice cup of herbal tea instead. Much safer.

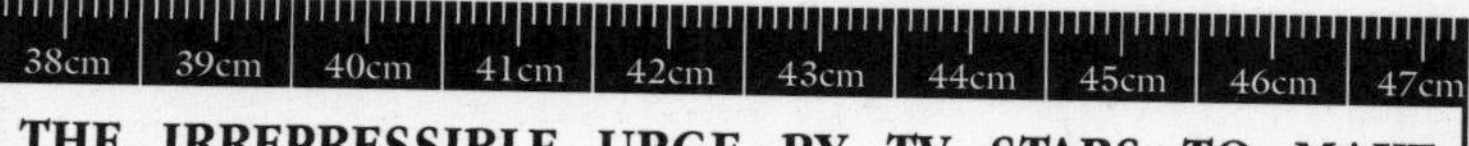

THE IRREPRESSIBLE URGE BY TV STARS TO MAKE EXERCISE VIDEOS

Angela Griffin's *Dance Mix Workout*

Anne Diamond – *A New You*

Barbara Windsor's *The Windsor Workout*

Beverley Callard – *Lasting Results* (qualified exercise instructor)

Carol Vorderman *Kick Start Detox and Exercise Plan*

Coronation Street – *Funk Fit*

Dancercise with Lucy Benjamin

Danniella Westbrook's *Better Body Workout*

Everyday Pilates with Fern Britton

Geri Halliwell *Body Yoga*

Hollyoaks *Dance Workout*

Ibiza Workout with Patsy Palmer

Leah Bracknell – *Yoga & You*

Linda Barker's *Simple Yoga*

Nell McAndrew – *Maximum Impact* (qualified exercise instructor)

Penny Smith's *Yoga Masterclass*

The Girls From Liberty X – *Toned*

Tone & Tease with Abi Titmuss

Tracey Shaw's *Salsacise*

*Ultimate Body Workou*t – Penny Lancaster (qualified exercise instructor)

*Walk Off The Pound*s With Lorraine Kelly

Zoe Lucker's Little Black Dress Workout

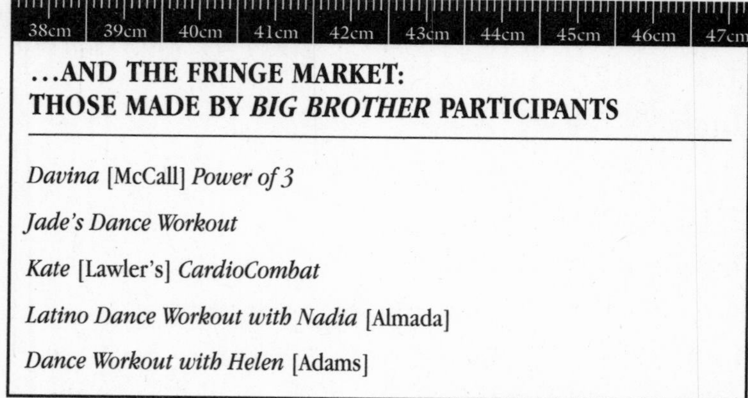

**...AND THE FRINGE MARKET:
THOSE MADE BY *BIG BROTHER* PARTICIPANTS**

Davina [McCall] *Power of 3*

Jade's Dance Workout

Kate [Lawler's] *CardioCombat*

Latino Dance Workout with Nadia [Almada]

Dance Workout with Helen [Adams]

**WHAT THE FITNESS QUEEN DID NEXT:
THINGS YOU DIDN'T KNOW ABOUT JANE FONDA**

1. She was born in 1937, and christened Lady Jayne Seymour Fonda because she was a distant relation of Henry VIII's wife Lady Jane Seymour.

2. As a later role model of health and fitness to millions of women, Fonda didn't start out too well in the good example department. When she went to college she became addicted to Dexedrine, which she had taken to suppress her appetite. In New York in the late 1950s, she lived on a diet of 'cigarettes, coffee, speed and strawberry yoghurt'. When she moved to Paris and married director Roger Vadim, she says, 'I ceased eating except for the crusts of his bread and the rinds of his Camembert.'

3. Her first foray into fitness was inadvertent – it was revealed in her autobiography that her first marriage also saw her being thrust into regular threesome sex with Vadim and prostitutes he summoned for the occasion. 'I took my cues from him,' she wrote, 'and threw myself into the threesome with the skill, energy and enthusiasm of

the actress that I am. If this was what he wanted, I would give it to him – in spades.'

4. She only went into fitness videos later, thinking she might raise $10,000 because, after her highly publicised peace activism during the Vietnam War, she was shunned by film studios as a communist and couldn't find work.

5. Her first fitness video, released in 1982, remains the biggest-selling video of all time in the US, selling an extraordinary 17 million copies. That and the 19 other videos that followed in the next 13 years made Fonda the First Lady of fitness and netted her a company that had a turnover of almost £400m a year in the 1980s.

6. All 20 videos have recently been relaunched on DVD.

7. Fonda didn't owe all of her figure to exercise, however much that might have appeared to be the case. At the height of her fame as an aerobics queen, she had breast implants inserted, then removed, and a rumoured operation to take out her lowest ribs in order to give herself a smaller waist.

8. Meanwhile she was still battling bulimia, a cycle of binge eating and vomiting as many as nine times a day, that started when she was 13 and carried on well into her 40s. 'For 25 years I could never put a forkful of food in my mouth without feeling fear,' she explained.

9. She also had less-acknowledged battles with alcohol, which saw her give up entirely at the beginning of 2004, reputedly in the wake of an ultimatum from her children.

10. After years of gruelling exercise, she's had to get a hip replaced, but is otherwise undimmed by age; now getting back into films and enjoying the single life after three husbands. Fonda says she is proud of her 'new-found serenity'.

38cm | 39cm | 40cm | 41cm | 42cm | 43cm | 44cm | 45cm | 46cm | 47cm

KNOW YOUR LINGO: NUTRITIONIST VS DIETITIAN

■ Even though they are the new gurus of our age, quoted authoritatively on every book cover and magazine page, pretty much anyone can, without qualification, call themselves a nutritionist, a nutritional therapist or a clinical nutritionist.

■ 'Dietitian', unlike 'nutritionist' is a protected name, and the only state-recognised nutrition licence in the UK at the moment.

■ Dietitians all belong to the British Dietetic Association (BDA), have to register with the health professionals' council and need to have a recognised degree.

■ The Nutrition Society is the nearest body nutritionists have to the BDA – and each recognises the other's qualifications. It is a professional body that has around 850 sufficiently qualified nutritionists (at least a nutrition degree) registering on a voluntary basis.

■ The British Association for Nutritional Therapy (BANT) is less demanding in its credentials – some of its 1,000 members are still students – while some experts criticise some of the courses recognised by BANT as qualifications as being too weak in biochemistry, physiology or epidemiology.

■ In layman's terms, therefore, you'd be safer choosing your nutritionist from the BDA or the Nutrition Society than from BANT.

■ In 2003, the Department of Health said that nutritional therapy was unlikely to be of sufficient risk to the public to require statutory regulation.

■ High-profile nutritional gurus who are not registered, or only registered with BANT, include Dr Gillian McKeith, Patrick Holford and 'food doctor' Ian Marber.

HOW TO CHOOSE A CELEBRITY FITNESS VIDEO

'The key is to look past the celebrity and read the back of the video to see who's devised the workout,' advises Ragdale Hall's health and fitness consultant Dean Hodgkin. 'If it hasn't been created by a fitness professional then be wary. No one would be stupid enough to make a video that wasn't safe; the issue is how effective the programme is. If it's been designed by an expert, you can have more confidence it will get results. A lot of celebrity videos tend to be themed along the lines of dance and yoga, but try to find one that offers cardio, strength training and then some flexibility work, so you're getting a well-rounded workout.'

WEIGHTY WORDS

The obsessive nature of dieting: Jack Nicholson, in the film *As Good As It Gets*, taking delivery of a Complan takeaway, 'But Tuesdays is banana flavour. Where's my banana flavour? You sent me strawberry'.

I bought all those celebrity exercise videos. I love to sit and eat cookies and watch them.

Dolly Parton

Breathing at my side, that heavy animal
That heavy bear that sleeps with me,
Howls in his sleep for a world of sugar
A sweetness intimate as the water's clasp.

Delmore Schwartz: *The Heavy Bear That Goes With Me*

A HOUSEWIVES' TALE

Jean Nidetch was a suburban New York housewife and mother of two, who struggled both mentally and physically to gain control of her weight problem since childhood. Sarah Watson was a food and nutrition graduate turned stay-at-home-mum who had never really accepted how overweight she was. One invented Weight Watchers from the kitchen table of her Brooklyn home and turned it into the world's leading weight-loss programme; the other went for a rainy walk with a neighbour in Surrey, wandered into Weight Watchers and lost 42lb (3st) in her first seven months, going on to become the most senior Brit in the organisation, personally launching its most recent system, 'Switch'.

Both have the neat, slightly padded look of middle-aged women who hold their figures rigidly in check: Nidetch hasn't touched a dessert in decades though she admits to a weakness for frozen yoghurt. In Nidetch's case, the eye is distracted by an alarming helmet of hair, a halo of unlikely blonde, and the messianic gleam of the truly committed health professional. In our celebrity-obsessed world, neither look glam or glossy enough to have, between them, transformed millions of women's lives. Yet, Nidetch and Watson, you get our *Fat, So?* Gold Medal for Role Models: go straight to the head of the class.

THE PETRA PAN OF THE FITNESS WORLD

We think she goes to bed in a cryogenic casket, only thawing occasionally to pop out and make a new exercise video. How else could Rosemary Conley not look a day older today than she did 20 years ago when she first launched the now famous Hip and Thigh Diet? She is, hard as it is to imagine, now 58 and tiny: 5ft 2in and a svelte 112lb (8st), with perfectly styled honey-blonde hair and endless energy.

She has put on millions of pounds over the years, but they all went into her bank account not onto her thighs. *Complete Hip and Thigh* – which she formulated after she had gallstones and her doctor told her to go on a strictly low-fat diet – alone sold two million copies. And the Rosemary Conley Diet and Fitness Clubs – books, classes, food ranges, a magazine – that she launched in 1993 now turn over £10m, having recently gained 30% more followers in just one year. Her latest DVD – the simply named *Rosemary Conley* – is one of no fewer than 13 exercise videos by her that are still available.

Now home for Rosemary and her second husband Mike is a seventeenth-century Gloucestershire manor, where she plays tennis, gardens, has the occasional indulgent taste of ice-cream and attends an exercise class twice a week. 'I'm lucky to be able to afford these things,' she says, 'but even if I couldn't I'd still want to make the most of myself.' We could hate her but we won't. We might just admit to hoping there's a picture in the attic of the manor house that shows a Rosemary both wrinkly and rippling in fat.

WEIGHTY WORDS

If you saw me first thing in the morning, you wouldn't recognise me. I believe that any woman can look good if she's willing to put the work in.

Rosemary Conley

It takes six months to get in shape and two weeks to get out of shape. As soon as you know this, you can stop being angry about other things in life and only be angry about this.

Rita Rudner

WEIGHTY WORDS

I really don't think I need buns of steel. I'd be happy with buns of cinnamon.

Ellen DeGeneres

Life is motion.

Aristotle

38cm 39cm 40cm 41cm 42cm 43cm 44cm 45cm 46cm 47cm

THAT TONGUE TEST: WHAT GILLIAN MCKEITH SAYS YOUR TONGUE SAYS ABOUT YOU

1. Does your tongue have a line down the middle? Weak digestion, feeling bloated, suffering from gas and indigestion. Brown rice, avocado and tofu as part of a 'You Are What You Eat' food-combining course of eight weeks.

2. Does your tongue have teeth marks round the side? Spleen weakness and nutrient deficiencies, feeling tired all the time, gassy and bloated. High nutrient foods like blue-green algae, alfalfa and hemp should top up the energy battery that is your spleen.

3. Does your tongue have a bright red tip? Emotional upset or bodily stress – either way you'll need B vitamins to calm it all down.

4. Is your tongue sore? Vitamin B6 deficiency and low niacin and/or iron levels – drink nettle or dandelion teas and eat food rich in B6, like sunflower seeds, brown rice, buckwheat and avocados.

5. Does your tongue appear dotted or coated with yellow? Liver stagnation – foods like kohlrabi, broccoli, cauliflower, flax seeds, hemp seeds and sunflower seeds should stop the liver performing its detox function sluggishly; good old nettle and dandelion teas too.

Taken from Gillian McKeith's *You Are What You Eat Cookbook*

THE FLIP SIDE OF EXERCISE

More than an hour of strenuous exercise a day saps fertility. The endorphins that make a woman feel good when they work out can interfere with ovulation. If body fat falls below 22%, the body doesn't believe you can support a baby and so suppresses fertility hormones. For men, those who are cyclists should check their saddles and suspension regularly: 88% of men cycling more than 3,000 miles (4,828km) a year had problems with their sperm counts.

Anyone doing high-impact exercise (running, tennis, tough aerobics) more than four times a week should watch out: when your foot strikes the ground during exercise, it does so at a force up to three times your weight. Constant pounding wears away cartilage, leading to painful osteoarthritis. Eating omega-3 oil fish acids helps.

People on weight-loss regimes, especially crash dieters, have often depleted their calcium levels. Moderate impact exercise strengthens bones, but training to excess messes with your oestrogen levels, causing the bones to release calcium and increasing risk of osteoporosis.

Up to two hours a day of exercise decreases your risk of infections by up to 30%, but more than this means the white blood cells that fight bacteria will lose their ability to do so.

Weekend warrior types sit around all week then go bananas at the weekend causing torn muscles. Production of free radicals increases 200-fold as we exercise; if the effort is only sporadic, the body's neutralising system isn't fired up leading to a free radicals' attack on soft tissue and muscle fibre, leading to aches and pains. Always warm up muscles with stretches before exercise – and cool down after.

People who are extremely inactive are more than 30 times more likely to have a heart attack, but take care about diving into exercise, because this could actually give you that heart attack. As little as 30 minutes' walking a day can lower heart disease risk by up to 40%.

JUST GO WITH THE FLOW

It's nice to know that even famously clever people can occasionally lose the plot. Cherie Blair, leading barrister, wife and helpmeet to the prime minister, was reported to have taken up 'thought field therapy' to help her lose weight. It's not the first time she's gone wacky: a few years ago, Cherie lost a stone with face-reading diet guru Elizabeth Gray Gibaud. She also became a client of her friend and handmaiden Carole Caplin, at Caplin's alternative health clinic Holistix, for holistic health remedies and diet advice. Lilias Curtin, who prefers to be known as a 'complimentary practitioner' (does that mean she pays you lots of compliments while she's treating you, or that the treatment is free? Facetious? Us?) rather than a therapist, shines a lamp containing sapphires and emeralds onto the body – the spleen, heart, lungs, kidney – to unblock energy lines and getting the blood to flow. At the end of each session, Mrs Blair pays her £120 and presumably goes back to work, energy unblocked, blood flowing and thinking thin thoughts.

YOU KNOW IT MAKES SENSE

You don't need a workout guru to tell you that exercise is the key to weight loss and a longer, better life. We now know that people who engage in at least moderate levels of activity were found to live longer than those who didn't, regardless of their weight. Even if they are slim, sedentary people die earlier, in new research mirrored by the findings of a British study carried out among 15,000 civil servants in the 1970s. And don't let being overweight stop you becoming active: actually, being slightly overweight makes you a better exerciser because the extra weight you carry means you use up more calories than a thin person doing the same activity. The cut-off point for physical activity – it is now claimed – should not occur until someone is truly obese, with a BMI that tops 40.

CELEBRITY SLIMMERS

Nobody would be a celebrity if they weren't severely damaged. We're just looking for all the love we never got as children. Nobody should look up to us, we're basically circus freaks.

Roseanne Barr

It's nice to know we aren't alone. Let's look at it that way. Let's not get hot under the collar about the fact that, every day, column inches are swamped by one or other celebrity actress, pop star or model telling us all about her diet travails when the chances are she started out thinner than we could ever dream of. Let's not get bitter. Let's focus on the fact that there are women out there who seem to have it all – looks, career, money, hunky other half – and yet they spend even more time worrying about their figure than we do.

Suddenly the playing field looks more level, doesn't it? We can even empathise with them – which makes us feel good – and, let's admit it, there's a craven part of us that picks up an article about Kate Winslet losing weight on the Prod Your Own Face Diet and wonders, since it worked for her, if it could possibly work for us, too. We're not alone; when celebrities endorse a diet, the paparazzi (and the diet's sales figures) go into overdrive. Look at Jennifer Aniston: according to our columnists, she 'swears by' not only the Atkins Diet, but also the Zone and, latterly, the Coconut Diet. Poor thing, no wonder she's wasting away. Of course, we wouldn't want to be cynical, but the chance to grab some column inches while you lose some hip inches must surely also play a part.

Look at Catherine Zeta Jones: even when she denies – crossly and vociferously, threatening to sue – that she has ever endorsed or even been on the Atkins Diet, we still get pages and pages of coverage: endless pictures of CZJ looking gorgeous and frothy wondering copy along the lines of: 'How does she do it?' Result for Mrs Douglas, methinks.

Then there's that particular source of enjoyment in the slight sense of crossness when we see a celebrity 'letting go' of themselves. 'Celebrity is as celebrity does,' as oozed by Gilderoy Lockhart, the star-worshipping wizard in *Harry Potter and the Chamber of Secrets*, so how dare they get lardy? Their entire existence depends on looking fabulous on red carpets, being ready for their close-up, swanking about in designer garb – generally giving the rest of us something to envy, and aspire to. They're loaded beyond our wildest dreams so if, God forbid, things get blubbery, then they have the cash to throw at chefs, nutritionists, personal trainers and PAs to order their food for them, going ahead of them and hiding all carbs and ice-cream away from them.

They have no excuse to be fat – not like we do: they're not busy, stressed, deskbound and hard up. So when the likes of Kirstie Alley, Jade Goody, Kerry Katona, Gail Porter and that car crash of a person, Anna Nicole Smith, start piling on the pounds, we feel justified in tut-tutting. After all, girls, slimness equals power in both Hollywood and the charts – power and success.

Then there's the other end of the scale: the awful, but awfully tempting, schadenfreude and glee when celebrities lose the plot and get too thin. Oh, the self-righteousness of the media when confronted by the 'lollipop ladies': aren't they setting a bad example for young girls? Isn't it shocking that so-and-so has a ribcage you could play a xylophone on? Ooh, look at those knobbly knees!

Well, we think you'll be delighted to hear that we are not going to shy away from such atrocities; we are not going to be held back by conscience or consideration for celebrities' feelings; we're just pulling our gloves off and getting deep down and dirty into the underworld of celebrity slimming, analysing those whose names come up again and again on the magazine health and beauty diet pages, the yummy mummies who lose their entire baby weight and then some about three minutes after giving birth and the yo-yo dieters among the rich and famous. Come on, join us. You know you want to.

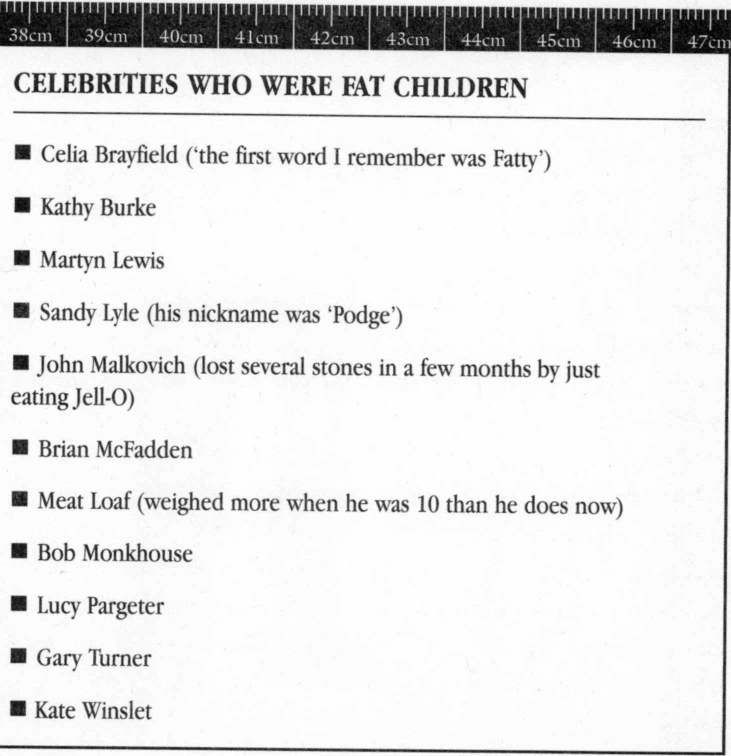

CELEBRITIES WHO WERE FAT CHILDREN

- Celia Brayfield ('the first word I remember was Fatty')
- Kathy Burke
- Martyn Lewis
- Sandy Lyle (his nickname was 'Podge')
- John Malkovich (lost several stones in a few months by just eating Jell-O)
- Brian McFadden
- Meat Loaf (weighed more when he was 10 than he does now)
- Bob Monkhouse
- Lucy Pargeter
- Gary Turner
- Kate Winslet

..IT'S NOT THAT THE MULTIVITAMINS ALOE VERA AND "ENERGY ENHANCING CRYSTALS" WILL DO ANY HARM... IT'S JUST THAT YOU MIGHT FIND FOOD A LOT CHEAPER!

BEEFY DIVAS

When celebrities get fat, they often choose to do so in some style. Take Elizabeth Taylor, whose fluctuating figure dominated her public persona for 30-odd years and seven husbands, who managed to get fat on caviar. Buckets of the stuff, as director Mike Figgis discovered when he went round to cook dinner for her one night.

Elvis Presley's particular yen was for his famous Fool's Gold sandwiches – entire foot-long baguettes crammed with bacon, peanut butter and strawberry jam. Each one contained 42,000 calories – enough to feed a normal man for a fortnight – yet Elvis was eating two a day in the weeks before he died, sometimes flying late at night to the Denver restaurant where they were made, ordering a dozen, then flying home again.

This is chickenfeed next to Luciano Pavarotti, who was so worried about what he was going to eat while touring in China that he didn't just order in from his favourite Italian bistro; he had the entire restaurant packed up and transported to Beijing. While he flew, he allegedly demanded that entire rows of seats be removed from the first-class compartment of the aeroplane to accommodate his bulk; for which he thanked the cabin crew by distributing entire wheels of cheese to each of them.

Sometimes, though, the weight gain is more prosaic: the late Marlon Brando was once hospitalised for eating too much ice-cream; John Travolta's fondness for macaroni-and-cheese ready meals meant he put on more weight than his wife, Kelly Preston, when she was pregnant with their son, Jett. It was the Andy Capp-style combination of pies and beer that did it for Robbie Williams. He now controls his weight, he says, with 80 cigarettes a day, and the P-Filling Diet. 'It's just the pie filling I eat now. I leave the crust.' Kids, don't try this at home.

DOUGHNUT

Beware the overprotectiveness of the celebrity dieter's entourage. At the premiere of her film, *Down with Love*, Renée Zellweger was 'chubbing up' to play in the Bridget Jones sequel. An over-anxious PR woman, suspecting a stunt might be played on the actress, ran up to one journalist and demanded to know if there was a doughnut in his bag. 'If you produce a doughnut for Renée, you'll be escorted from the premises!' she fired at him. Soon after, the bemused – and innocent – reporter was 'disinvited' from all red carpet events organised by that PR company.

DID YOU NOTICE?

In January 2003, an airbrushed image of Kate Winslet on the cover of *GQ* magazine caused an uproar. Suddenly her legs looked twice the length and her silhouette carved down in several places. But the down-to-earth star was furious because the magazine had done it without her approval and it appeared to undermine her attempts to look natural. In the accompanying interview, Kate had said: 'All the men I've ever spoken to like girls to have an arse on them. So why is it that women think in order to be adored they have to be thin? I'm certainly not a sex symbol who doesn't eat.' Go, girlfriend.

THE FAT SLAGS

Even though it featured Geri Halliwell and Ralf Little, and starred Sophie Thompson and *Smack the Pony* actress Fiona Allen, the movie version of *Fat Slags* was so bad that *Viz* editor Graham Dury announced he was going to drop the foul-mouthed pair. But the popularity of *Fat Slags* was more enduring than even their creators had predicted and, after an onslaught from distraught fans pleading for the lardy twosome to be reinstated, Dury relented and their 14-year history of fun, filth and fattening-up looks set to continue.

BLAME IT ON SHOWBUSINESS

A recent survey of GPs carries the warning that celebrities are actually to blame for our bulging waistlines. Eight out of 10 doctors pointed the finger at 'celebrity food fads' for creating a nation of yo-yo dieters and attacked the media for holding up images of skinny stars as something to aim for. Pull-out diet sheets from magazines were also criticised for encouraging a 'ridiculous ideal'. One said: 'Celebrities are often taken in themselves by the latest diet crazes and seem to reinvent their eating regimes as often and as easily as they reinvent their own image. It doesn't make for a sensible or sustainable healthy living plan for the rest of us.'

38cm 39cm 40cm 41cm 42cm 43cm 44cm 45cm 46cm 47cm

BOOTYLICIOUS: THE FAT-BOTTOMED GIRLS THAT MAKE THE ROCKIN' WORLD GO ROUND

- Beyoncé: there's a fine line between love and weight.
- Emma Bunton: bouncing Baby Spice occasionally tips over into chubbiness.
- Britt Ekland: on the Beverley Hills Diet was doubled over with diarrhoea when she suffered this absurd eating regime.
- Nigella Lawson: still a Domestic Goddess with a Mount Olympus of a bottom.
- Jennifer Lopez: always celebrated for her ramp of a rump, sometimes looks more of a lump.
- Shakira: shows us how, with a tiny waist, you can get away with a big asset.
- Liv Tyler: undeniably gorgeous, but undeniably borderline in the fluctuating weight department.

A FAD LOT OF USE: NEARLY DEADLY DIETS

Detox – GMTV star Fiona Phillips was nearly killed on a detox diet by an allergic reaction to pumpkin seeds.

Atkins – Claire Sweeney blamed the high-protein diet for giving her a kidney infection – and Corrie star Denise Welch was left weak and sick after spending two weeks on the plan for a documentary.

Fruit Flush – Victoria Beckham was sick as a dog when she tried a strawberry-only regime during Euro 2004.

Pineapple Diet – *I'm a Celebrity* model Catalina Guirado fell ill after a string of diets, including eating just three pineapples a day – the enzymes were supposed to burn fat, but left her with stomach ulcers.

YUMMY MUMMIES

Some celebrities are very kind to us mere mortals. For just a few months, we can see what they would look like as normal people struggling with their weight. Of course, while they're looking 'normal' they also just happen to be having babies but, hey, at least they are putting themselves through the indignity of pregnancy, even if only momentarily or, in Victoria Beckham's pregnancy with Cruz, entirely invisibly, hidden away under ponchos and large handbags.

Yes, these are the yummy mummies, the celebrities for whom the press coverage is entirely schizophrenic. One minute, the media is shouting how radiant the mum-to-be is, and isn't it great that she's thrown caution to the winds and pigged out on anything they fancy? Next up, post-birth, is breathless admiration for how quickly they've regained their figures before veering into tutting disapproval, backed by pseudo-medical expert opinion, that they've done so too quickly, that they haven't given their bodies a chance to recover, that they're setting an unrealistic example to other, more struggling, mums. And through it all these mummies just look, well, yummy.

Catherine Zeta Jones: When Mrs Douglas accepted her Oscar for *Chicago* in 2003, she weighed nearly 196lb (14st). OK, she was about to give birth any second to daughter Carys, but she still weighed nearly 196lb. And she looked fantastic. The Welsh-born valley girl is about as yummy as a mummy gets and she insists she's terribly sensible about the diet that got her back down to 140lb (10st), to the extent where she threatened to sue the Atkins Corporation when it was claimed she was on the carbohydrate-free eating regime. She says she did it all with a few slimming sheets from her mum Pat's Swansea slimming club and old-fashioned determination. 'I love chocolate, ice-cream and cakes,' she has said. 'I look after myself without being crazy or a bore about it.' But do we believe her? She wasn't so sensible with her first pregnancy, when she gained 56lb (4st), then within just four months she had dieted and worked out her way down to a size 10 wedding dress. She also vows she hates the gym and insists she stays in shape by swimming, playing golf, dancing – and fencing for her reprisal of her role in *The Legend of Zorro*. Call us cynical, but we think there's more to Miz Jones's maintenance regime than she would have us believe. No matter, she looks darn good on it.

Madonna is almost too toned and scary-looking for yummy mummy status, but she certainly qualifies on the iron self-control front. After the birth of daughter Lourdes in 1996, Madonna went on a crash diet of dry popcorn, followed by a punishing regime of weights, cycling and running to lose 28lb (2st) in eight weeks – to dazzle in a size 8 dress at the premiere of *Evita*. Four years later, when son Rocco was born, the then 42-year-old adopted a gentler approach of yoga, a macrobiotic diet and breastfeeding. Six weeks later she was 105lb (7½st), flashing her famous washboard stomach on stage at the MTV Music Awards, and has maintained the same sinewy, tightly disciplined body shape ever since.

38cm 39cm 40cm 41cm 42cm 43cm 44cm 45cm 46cm 47cm

SNEAK A PEEK: CELEBS WITH CELLULITE

Ever since that famous picture of Princess Diana going to the gym revealed that the most beautiful woman in the world had cellulite, the long-distance lenses of the paparazzi have been pointing down at famous nether regions to reveal that stars also have orange-peel thighs.

- Beyoncé
- Cindy Crawford
- Melanie Griffiths
- Jerry Hall
- Nicole Kidman
- Keira Knightley
- Britney Spears

Davina McCall: After the birth of second daughter, Tilly, the chatelaine of *Big Brother* was feeling more like Big Mother, having put on 25lb (1st 11lb) and gone up to a size 16. Then, in a strange inverse equation common among famous mums, Davina became a stone lighter than she was before becoming pregnant. That would be because of the three workouts a week, spurred on by two personal trainers (one to yell in each ear?), the three balanced (tiny) meals a day and, now, yawn, the exercise DVD that has resulted, called *Power of 3*. Yes, Davina, the Power of having three hours a day in which to think about making yourself slimmer. She even achieved the ultimate accolade: being criticised in the tabloids for being too thin. Result, as they'd say in the *Big Brother* house. With a third baby, McCall is now taking this Power of 3 thing a little literally... but still looking enviably gorgeous.

Gwyneth Paltrow: The daughter of two of the world's other most famous macrobiotics was never going to be called Candy, Twinky or KrispyKreme, which is why we secretly weren't that surprised when Gwyneth and Chris named their firstborn Apple. What was more surprising was that Gwyneth turned out to be surprisingly human – having put on nearly 42lb (3st) over the pregnancy, she was caught in photos looking even a little bulgy around the middle, publicly delighting in the fact that, for the first time in her life she had breasts, hips and a tummy. At an awards ceremony, she won hearts and minds throughout Britain, by admitting that she was a member of the Spanx Pants Fan Club, those miracles of modern engineering whereby unwanted curves are hidden away under thick layers of hold-em-all-in Lycra underwear. She even ditched her strict macrobiotic diet, compromising with organic foods and avoiding sugar. 'I steer clear of candy because I don't think it has any energy in it,' she said. 'I just try not to eat any over-manufactured foods that aren't naturally welcome in my body.' Now also the mum of Moses, she's back to her whippety self, Spanx pants tossed away. But, hey, for a moment there she was almost one of us…

PLASTIC FANTASTIC?

She's plastic and hasn't even got real genitals but Barbie is the worst celebrity role model of them all. If she were lifesize, her vital statistics would be 39-23-33, she would stand at an absurd 7ft 2in and have a neck twice the length of that of an average human being.

WEIGHTY WORDS

Is there chicken in chickpeas?

Helen Adams, *Big Brother*

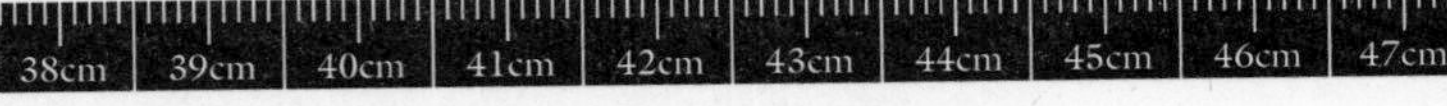

MAKE MINE A PEANUT BUTTER PIZZA: FAMOUS MUMS' PREGNANCY CRAVINGS

- Zoe Ball: lettuce and fruit
- Victoria Beckham: gherkins
- Cate Blanchett: sardines
- Mel B: peanut butter, cheesecake, ice-cream and chips
- Ms Dynamite: strawberry flavoured Ben & Jerry's ice-cream
- Gloria Estefan – sweetened condensed milk
- Natasha Hamilton: sweet puddings and fried breakfasts
- Catherine Zeta Jones: beetroot (first time); Branston pickle and curry (second time)
- Ulrika Jonsson: digestive biscuits (third time)
- Madonna: butternut squash and sticky toffee puddings
- Davina McCall: Tabasco sauce and Coca-Cola (first time); radishes and Coca-Cola (second time)
- Melinda Messenger: cucumber
- Marie Osmond: grapefruit sorbet topped with sardines
- Fiona Phillips: cream, then mints
- Brooke Shields: extremely strong coffee and nutmeg
- Kate Winslet: fizzy cola sweets, blackcurrant juice and tomatoes

THE YO-YO

Yes, it's a child's toy, but for our purposes a yo-yo is that special class of celebrity whose weight veers from slim to fat and, usually, back again. It's one of those sadistic categories, where the media turn into moralistic governesses, poking and probing to see which side of the pendulum the poor benighted celebrity is on now. It doesn't reflect well on us public that we savour such reports, but it does reflect the self-same problem throughout dieting society: yo-yo-ing is experienced by nearly all dieters, especially those who originally sought rapid weight loss. So that's OK, then. Because it happens to us all, we're allowed to gloat when it happens to famous people because it makes them more like us. Phew. So read on.

Kirstie Alley made her larger-than-life comeback in *Fat Actress* and she seemed, for a moment, refreshingly different. She wasn't going to wriggle into the yo-yo dieting pigeonhole, she was just going to get fatter and fatter. Having said baldly that she was fat because, 'I ate too much. I had too big a party,' she pitched the show to TV execs with a vast box of 300 doughnuts. She gave interviews saying that to be fat was an intrinsic part of her ambition, 'As a young girl I'd say to my Dad, "I'm gonna grow up and have four cars, have a huge house and eat cake and batter for dinner every night."' So why have we put her in the yo-yo section? Because Kirstie Alley is now a career yo-yo-er. *Fat Actress*, be gone, she then got a $1m deal to write a humorous diet and lifestyle book, titled *How to Lose Your Ass and Regain Your Life* and, in shedding 5st, lost all the weight that had given her her comeback in the first place. But for how long will she stay a skinny mini?

Geri Halliwell has already swung back and forth a few times on the yo-yo front. The petite 5ft 1in singer went from being the chubbiest Spice Girl (not that that was very hard) to a gaunt yoga fanatic of 91lb (6½st). She admitted to having suffered from bulimic episodes since her teens. Now the mercurial pop-pixie is still super-fit but is back to some of her former curvaceousness and looks fantastic, even after giving birth to daughter Bluebell. In a poll, 60% of men said they thought Geri's voluptuousness make her sexier than Victoria Beckham's chic skinniness. Even though more words have been written about her weight than about her singing, she's even having the last laugh on that front: she holds the record for the most UK number ones by a female artist (if you add her solo hits to those of the Spice Girls). 'My dieting days are over,' she has announced. 'The more I try to diet, the bigger I get. Acceptance is the diet I'm on.' Watch this space.

Janet Jackson has fought the flab for years, actually admitting: 'My weight has been up and down like a yo-yo. I got teased all my life.' Next stop was a nutritionist whom she credits with having centred her between too thin and too plump, but admits that it's a constant battle. Not that we want to impose suffering on celebrities, but that's comforting to hear…

Oprah Winfrey has gone up and down the weight chart so many times that, rumour has it, she doesn't just have a 'thin' and a 'fat' wardrobe, she has 'thin' and 'fat' *rooms.* In 1988, Oprah, dragging a wagon piled with 67lb of fat, announced on her show that she had lost that much. Only four years later, the billionairess was at her heaviest, weighing 238lb (17st). After a tough diet and exercise regime, she is currently svelte, at just over 10st (140lb) and has reportedly commissioned a nude bronze of herself to capture this weight for posterity.

Renée Zellweger must be both pin-up girl and darts target for dieters everywhere. This is because even though she put on – then took off – 28lb (2st) to play famously weight-obsessed Bridget Jones, she's not actually a yo-yo dieter. Both her weight gain and her weight loss were entirely deliberate. For the former she ate vast amounts of doughnuts, fettucine alfredo and chocolate, washed down with pints of Guinness. For the latter, she used Atkins first time round, then followed in Jennifer Aniston's footsteps to try the Zone. Both times she ended up on the scrawny side of slim – and that's where she'll stay because, as she says, 'this is the weight I've been since I came to Hollywood, and this is the weight I like to be.' What no one ever dares point out is that Renée is cursed with a face that is fatter than her body – and it's clear to us that she's chosen to go with favouring the face rather than the figure.

38cm 39cm 40cm 41cm 42cm 43cm 44cm 45cm 46cm 47cm

STARS WHO HAVE ADMITTED TO SUFFERING FROM EATING DISORDERS

Victoria Beckham	Davina McCall
Kate Beckinsale	Mary-Kate Olsen
Michelle Collins	Sharon Osbourne
Jane Fonda	Gail Porter
Uri Geller	Christina Ricci
Geri Halliwell	Emma Thompson
Sir Elton John	Kate Winslet

THEY CAN'T EVEN EXERCISE LIKE NORMAL PEOPLE

Victoria Beckham recovers her bounce on a trampoline for a whole body, cardiovascular workout, improving flexibility and strength. Just 10 minutes burns 125 calories, which is equivalent to a 30-minute jog.

Jennifer Ellison tops up her fitness with inline skating, a great cardio workout which improves balance and tones up lower-body muscles. In 30 minutes, you can skate off 220 calories.

Madonna, when she's not cycling to the Kabbalah centre, likes to hula hoop, which is a great way to tone up the tum and improve motion in the knees and hips. Burns 145 calories in half an hour.

Kate Moss likes swinging in the playground, which is a great way to banish bingo wings. Burns 126 calories in half an hour.

38cm 39cm 40cm 41cm 42cm 43cm 44cm 45cm 46cm 47cm

NAUGHTY BUT NICE: STARS' PIG-OUT OF CHOICE

- Christina Aguilera: Wendy's Big Bacon Classic – her manager calls her the 'fast food queen'
- Mariah Carey: doughnuts – she loves them when she's on tour
- Cameron Diaz: burger and fries
- Fergie from Black Eyed Peas: pizza
- Michael Jackson: Kentucky Fried Chicken – at any hour of the day or night
- Jordan: a Big Mac
- Britney Spears: chocolate – she reckons it's better than sex
- Uma Thurman: desserts

HURLEY-BURLEY

For an actress/model who's never actually done a great deal – as she says, 'Being able to squeeze myself into tiny clothes is how I earn my living,' – the column inch count on Elizabeth Hurley and her figure is impressive.

What is equally impressive is the steely determination that La Hurley obviously brings to her weight-management routine. First there was the post-pregnancy weight loss, when Liz went into purdah at Elton John's Windsor mansion and didn't appear until seven weeks later, lithe, tanned and svelte after a regime of bootcamp exercise and watercress soup.

After the birth of her son, Damian, Liz lost almost 56lb (4st), becoming an enviable size 8. The comforting thing about Liz is that she really works for her figure: not for her, the blithe swanning about of Jordan or Anna Friel, both of whom were back to whippety thinness within weeks of their babies being born.

According to loose talk, even when Liz does eat, she dines on a nursery plate, with doll-sized cutlery to make her portion-controlled food look larger. Most recently there was a gasp of tabloid horror at the revelation that she only actually has one meal a day – dinner – and snacks during the day. 'Six raisins for lunch!' screamed the headlines. Forget the lunch part; since when were six raisins a snack? Aren't raisins just the inbetweeny grazing part between the snacks? And there's the problem.

Beach holiday snaps of Liz and boyfriend Arun Nayar show her to be in enviably good shape for someone into her fifth decade, but she's not exactly fading away. If she basically has to starve herself to look like this – she admits that, 'I go to bed hungry' – what would she look like if she ate like the rest of us? Is this a comforting or a horrifying thought?

THE DUCHESS OF PORK

This was only one of the cruellest headlines – 'Beached Whale', 'The Fat White Woman Whom Nobody Loves' and the mean *Sun* poll where 80% of Englishmen said they would rather sleep with a goat than her, being other low points that Sarah Ferguson, the Duchess of York, has had with the media and the public. Now she is anything but Fat Fergie – as the ambassador of Weight Watchers in America, she has kept off the 42lb (3st) she lost with them, is now an enviable dress size 8-10 and, when caught offguard by callous paparazzi, even looks a little gaunt around the face area. She only nibbles at food and goes running whenever she gets the chance.

To boost her system occasionally, she books into the exclusive Mayr Health Clinic in Austria where, for £2,000 a day, she's allowed only 600 calories a day, undergoes 'intestinal regeneration' (yikes!) and lives in a bathrobe all day. At other times, she is soignée and elegant, usually dressed in slimming black, and impeccably well-behaved. Who would have thought that the bouncing, clumsy, braying redhead of yesteryear could have turned into today's elegant, svelte and gracious Duchess? That the ugly duckling could turn into a swan? It's a heart-warming fairytale, albeit a poignant modern one, where the damsel in distress starts with the prince and ends up running a flourishing business. 'I had to be completely stripped down of the old Sarah in order to be the new Sarah. I had to be demolished. And I was. I was demolished.'

WEIGHTY WORDS

Eat up your greens! There are thousands of children in Hollywood with eating disorders.

John Callaghan

EATING
DISORDER
CLINIC
NAF

LOLLIPOP LADIES: 'WORRYINGLY THIN' STARS

With heads bigger than their bodies – hence the monicker, 'Lollipop Ladies' – they're underweight, all with a BMI of less than 18.5, and, in some cases, are clearly starving themselves for stardom. A massive 85% of doctors feel that those who follow these celebrities' faddy eating plans are endangering their long-term health. One doctor in a survey said: 'Celebrities are not nutritionists. Many are actually underweight and under-nourished, but they don't even realise it. Or if they do, they have a vested interest in looking "perfect" and don't care about the long-term problems – osteoporosis, iron deficiency anaemia, fertility and, worst case scenario, premature death.'

Victoria Beckham: Even she admits she has 'absolutely no bum at all' and insists her new Mediterranean diet has got her into great shape, but medical experts say she is still dangerously thin.

Lara Flynn Boyle: While she was snapped on the beach looking like skin and bone, LFB was busy insisting to the press that she ate: 'roast beef, peas in mashed potatoes, escargot, caviar, peanut butter and jelly'. Go figure. Recent beach pictures show the actress has filled out a little and is now a healthier size 8.

Sophie Dahl: Having trimmed down from a size 16 to a size 8, Sophie swapped her 'curvaceous beauty' and 38DD chest, for, as one commentator put it, 'stick-legs, no breasts and huge, frightened eyes. Now she really does look like Bambi.'

Britt Ekland: The iconic Bond girl now admits that periodic starving for roles back in the 1960s and 1970s have been pinpointed as the cause of her osteoporosis. 'I do worry terribly about today's female celebrities, who are even thinner than our generation was.'

Teri Hatcher: Although she vehemently denies that she is the 'Desperately Shrinking Housewife', Teri nonetheless appears to be disappearing fast. 'The only thing I'm guilty of is being too athletic and refusing to eat garbage. I eat a lot of fruit.'

Eva Herzigova: 'I love food. I live on bread, cheese and salami. Chips are my favourite.' At the time she said this she was photographed looking blue-lipped, gaunt, grey and bony, with hardly an echo of the 'Hello, boys' décolletage that made this Wonderbra girl one of the world's favourite hoarding pin-ups.

Kate Hudson: She got back into shape within four months of giving birth, but a year later was pictured looking like a walking pipe cleaner, with straggly hair and knobbly knees. Not a good look for Goldie's golden girl.

Nicole Kidman: Even though she's always been a string bean, Nicole then reputedly cut out starch and sugars from her diet, turning her into a social X-ray and a pale imitation of her already pale former self.

Lindsay Lohan: She says it's loss of baby fat and acid reflux, adding: 'Compared to a lot of actresses my age, I'm actually overweight.' But we say that with her suspiciously fluffy cheeks and forearms and jutting hipbones; she was starting to look unhealthy. More than 12,500 fans signed an online petition urging: 'Please, Lindsay, Eat!'

Nicole Ritchie: Once voluptuous, the adopted daughter of Lionel Ritchie has been visibly shrinking – going straight through shapely and heading for skeletal. She says she's just lost the weight she put on in drug rehab, but maybe she's competing with her fiancé, who also lost multiple stones from the days when he was a nerdy couch potato.

38cm 39cm 40cm 41cm 42cm 43cm 44cm 45cm 46cm 47cm

CHILD STARS WHO PROMOTED FOOD IN TV ADS

Drew Barrymore – Gainsburgers

Jessica Biel – Pringles crisps

Emma Bunton – Milky Bar

Keith Chegwin – Marathon bar (old name for Snickers)

Jeff Daniels – McDonalds

Sarah Michelle Gellar (Burger King: she couldn't say 'burger' so needed a speech coach)

Patsy Kensit – Birds Eye frozen peas

Michael Portillo – Ribena

Jonathan Ross – Rice Krispies

Kate Winslet – Sugar Puffs

38cm 39cm 40cm 41cm 42cm 43cm 44cm 45cm 46cm 47cm

CELEBS WHO HAVE SHED HALF THEIR BODY WEIGHT

- Roseanne Barr shed 196lb (14st) after stomach-stapling gastric surgery.
- Sharon Osbourne was another bypasser who lost 112lb (8st), which left her with so much surplus flesh, she needed plastic surgery to lift it.
- Carnie Wilson, of Wilson Phillips, halved her body weight within a year after a gastric bypass (shown live on the internet: nice!), but admits she still needs to diet.
- After years of yo-yo dieting, Victoria Wood lost 126lb (9st) by eating healthily and exercising regularly, but insists she isn't smug.

THE DIETARY EQUIVALENT OF THE RACHEL HAIRCUT

First she cut her hair – and hairdressers the world over made millions from replicating the Rachel Cut on their deluded clients. Now it's diets. When Jennifer Aniston puts her name to a diet, the sellers of said diet start planning their Christmas trip to the Caribbean.

When she was the unofficial poster girl for the Atkins Diet, the *New Atkins Diet Revolution* books walked out of the shops as fast as their new owners could waddle. Then she switched to the Zone, opting to have specially prepared Zone meals delivered to her home, and suddenly the Zone was the diet of Hollywood choice. Lately, she's been through more of a Divorce Diet, which is a harder sell to the fans, and she's even been criticised for looking too scrawny. We suspect that disciplined Jen doesn't let all the hubbub bother her.

'I used to eat everything that was bad for me,' she reveals. 'But then I stopped. I wasn't fat. I was just Greek and everyone knows Greeks are round with big bottoms and big boobs.' Not a description that springs to mind, but we're suckers for even the suggestion of low self-esteem from one of our favourite stars.

FIT TO POP IDOL

She's had spectacular success on Channel 4's *You Are What You Eat*, but GI bean guru Dr Gillian McKeith is now going for chart stardom with her recent celebrity case studies. First up was Brian McFadden, whom McKeith slimmed down from his Westlife whale days to a suitably gaunt, cheekboned look for his abortive attempt at going indie. The only trouble was, he then left his cuddly wife Kerry, who'd loved him when he was a porker, and matched his own new thin look to a new, thinner model in the form of Australian hottie Delta Goodrem (whereupon he promptly got fat again and Kerry got thin). Not that that was Dr Gillian's fault, of course.

SOLD OUT?

Celebrity sells but have celebrities sold out? Paying the likes of Jamie Oliver millions of pounds to front a supermarket's ad campaigns is one thing: Sainsbury's says that his campaign generated £1.12bn in sales and helped open people's eyes to the potential of fresh foods. Prunella Scales and Jane Horrocks's adverts for Tesco are arguably the most successful supermarket campaign ever, resulting in revenues of over £2bn. George Foreman was just another has-been boxer before he lent his name to an obscure kitchen appliance: now more than 30 million Lean Mean Fat-Reducing Grilling Machines have been sold worldwide.

DIET-RELATED NICKNAMES FOR CELEBRITIES IN THEIR SCHOOLDAYS

Sophie Anderton – Thunder Thighs

Cameron Diaz – Skeletor (because she was so skinny)

Leonardo DiCaprio – The Noodle

Liam Gallagher – Weetabix (as intelligent as?)

Bob Geldof – Liver Lips

Geri Halliwell – Pancake (because of her flat chest!)

Felicity Kendal – Fatty Foo

Sophia Loren – The Stick or Toothpick (because she was so thin)

Prince Edward – Jaws

Denise Richards – Fish Lips

Kate Winslet – Blubber

But now curbs on the use of celebrities promoting unhealthy food for children are planned to help tackle the growing problem of child obesity. Watchdogs want the likes of Gary Lineker to stop promoting crisps and lend his backing to something like an 'Eat an Apple' campaign. David Beckham has long and successfully been associated with Pepsi, Lawrence Dallaglio with McDonald's, Wayne Rooney with Coca-Cola and Steven Gerrard with Lucozade. But is using sportsmen, who presumably never actually touch the stuff they're promoting, the right message to give children?

In a *Which?* survey of 2,000 parents, 77% said that such marketing of children's foods and drinks increased the 'pester power' of children and made it difficult to refuse them – and 81% believed that stars should promote healthier foods to kids. 'To these celebrities it's just another sponsorship deal: to us, it's our children's teeth and long-term health,' said one. 'Surely it's not that much to ask that they give up promoting junk?' Children preferred wackier approaches: 'Maybe Gary Lineker should give away a free exercise video with his Walkers crisps?' said one questioned in the survey. 'How about free liposuction with every 10 McDonalds?' joked another.

MOST WEIRD CELEBRITY DIETER EVER

Sarah Miles drinking her own urine. No question.

WEIGHTY WORDS

I eat when I'm depressed and I eat when I'm happy. When I can't decide whether I'm tired or hungry I make the decision while I'm eating.

Oprah Winfrey

38cm | 39cm | 40cm | 41cm | 42cm | 43cm | 44cm | 45cm | 46cm | 47cm

REARS OF THE YEAR FROM THE PAST 10 YEARS

As awarded by the British jeans industry:

2005: Nell McAndrew and Will Young

2004: Alex Best and Aled Hadyn-Jones

2003: Natasha Hamilton and Ronan Keating

2002: Charlotte Church and Scott Wright

2001: Claire Sweeney and John Altman

2000: Jane Danson and Graham Norton

1999: Denise van Outen and Robbie Williams

1998: Carol Smillie and Frank Skinner

1997: Melinda Messenger and Gary Barlow

1996: Tracy Shaw

UP ON A SOAP BOX

It must be something in the soap, but TV starlets – both men and women – feel the need to play out their weight-loss dramas on the tabloid pages. Is it in their contract that their figures must fluctuate? 'Week 57: learn lines, get bad hair extensions, reveal new tattoo and gain eight pounds', thereby guaranteeing trashy mag coverstory and publicity for the programme? Take Lucy-Jo Hudson (one-time Katy Harris on *Coronation Street*) who found herself snacking at Corrie's 'butty wagon' on set. 'Before I knew it, I'd started eating a week's worth of food in one day.'

When Lucy-Jo went up to just under 154lb (11st) at 5ft 4in, she 'looked really beefy'. Weight Watchers ('I got bored'), Carol Vorderman's Detox for Life ('I couldn't live on it') and Gillian McKeith's You Are What You Eat, ('I just couldn't stick to seaweeds and nuts, it's too strict') soon followed in strict succession before she did a very un-soap-starry thing and employed her brother to get her into shape down the gym. Boxing, weight-training, cardiovascular work, swimming, yoga and body-pump – attention-span problem, anyone? – led to her shedding 21lb (1½st). Cue sparkly dress appearances at TV awards ceremonies. Everyone happy.

AND FINALLY… GOOD BONK, GOOD BODY

It's all very tabloid, but if famous people say these things, they must expect to have them quoted back at them. So we couldn't resist revealing those celebrities who owe their figures to a diet of sizzling sex. Kelly Brook says that sex is the only diet she's ever managed to stick to and that, 'it keeps me fit and healthy. What could be better than sex as part of your diet?' Nothing at all, says Martine McCutcheon: 'I owe my figure to yoga, swimming… and loads of sex!'

John Travolta reckons he shed 28lb (2st) on a love-based diet; Halle Berry says it helps if you make a racket at the same time: 'having noisy sex is a great way to stay healthy.' Sting and Trudie Styler have long been advocates of the healthy bonk, healthy body school of thought with Sting having a renowned taste for Tantric sex. Sex expert Anne Hooper is also a fan: 'Making love is a form of aerobic exercise. Just half an hour's nookie burns up 350 calories and is equivalent to 45 minutes' aerobics.' Of course it helps if it's George Clooney you're working up a sweat with but, hey, we can dream…

DIETING FOR MEN

I could be a vegetarian. There's no meat in beer, right?

Joey Tribbiani, *Friends*

Well, the Fat Lady is still singing and this time her tune is a well-known German ditty: schadenfreude. It's not nice of us to rub our hands together with glee and say, 'Welcome to the paranoia party, fellas!' but that's exactly what we're going to do. It's now official: men get fat, too. Even better, men now diet, too.

According to market researchers Mintel, one in four British men is currently on a diet – a rise of 50% in two decades. Projections for 2010 suggest that 75% of men will be overweight or obese by then and that by the middle of this century, men will be just as obsessed with dieting as women. The scales of justice will finally be balanced.

Perhaps we shouldn't crow too much, because there's more bad news for the boys. According to the Men's Health Forum, obesity in men is far more serious in terms of medical conditions than in women. Women tend to put fat on around the hips and backside. Men pork up around the gut, which produces metabolic syndrome, a triad of medical problems – increased blood pressure, diabetes and abnormal blood lipids – where a very small increase in any one of them produces a disproportionate amount of danger.

Traditionally the hunters, while women were the gatherers, men have suffered even more than their mates in our increasingly sedentary age. Sitting on their backsides all day doing nothing more than tapping on a keyboard and yelling at the odd intransigent client on the phone has done terrible things for the physique of a gender who should still be chasing down a buffalo with a spear.

Back in the bad old days, those with the ability to store excess energy efficiently and release it when needed for physical labour had a better chance of survival. Now that there is not the same need for the body to store and release energy – and with blokes burning off less excess energy than in their me-Tarzan days – those calories are just sitting around, chumming it up in the beer-belly department.

Men are increasingly aware that they are overweight, but winning men over to dieting is a totally different ball game to selling a regime to a woman. A survey by the Men's Health Forum found that many men were against seeking help to lose weight – regarding the slimming world as horrifyingly unmacho – so the Forum produced a health guide in the form of a car manual in an attempt to ram the message home: the *HGV Man Manual*, where the recommendation to seek advice from a GP is likened to sending a car for its MOT. Sometimes, you couldn't make this stuff up.

Of course, the commercial implications of this have not escaped the ever-hungry diet-book industry. Along with tongue-in-cheek diets like Men in Fur's Caveman Diet, come special promotions from the likes of Slim-Fast and other shake-based diets, capitalising on the notion that men would rather diet privately and surreptitiously, slurping slimming shakes and passing them off as protein shakes for their body-building programme.

WEIGHTY WORDS

My doctor has advised me to give up those intimate little dinners for four. Unless there are three people eating with me.

Orson Welles

MOST FAMOUS MALE DIETER

Drum roll for Mahatma Gandhi, please. It's the only roll he would ever have accepted. Even when Gandhi wasn't starving for protest reasons, he wasn't exactly the Crammer of Calcutta, confining himself to a daily ration of just 'three ounces of germinating wheat, three ounces of green leaves (pounded), three ounces of almonds reduced to a paste, two ounces of honey and six sour lemons.' We'd hazard a guess that here was a man who didn't exactly like food...

MR MUSCLE

Muscle dysmorphia or bigorexia is a new phenomenon among men slimmers: the practice whereby men exercise excessively in the mistaken view that their body is too puny. One in five British men is now a member of a gym. In America, they've gone one step beyond – combining over-intense gym usage with drugs. A Brown University survey of 1,000 teenagers found that, when presented with a range of images of male physiques, more than half of those questioned wanted a body shape that could only be achieved by using steroids.

MEN'S METABOLISM

There may be a gender difference in the metabolic response to exercise. If that sounds grand and technical that's because we're feeling rather tight-lipped about it and reluctant to expand. Basically, men have the advantage: if they work out and diet, they gradually lose more and more weight as the rate of metabolism rises in response to the exercise. In women, the rise is not significant: no matter how much we exercise, the total daily expenditure of calories doesn't actually increase, so it's just more of the same old, same old. In other words, IT'S NOT FAIR.

MALE CELEBRITIES PUBLICLY FIGHTING THE FLAB

■ Ben Affleck – trains with a guru on the 'Brain Diet' – 20% physical diet, 80% psychological belief in change – aka think yourself thin.

■ The Late Marlon Brando – on a typical day, crammed in 15,000 calories; lost some in his own customised diet but died still massively overweight.

■ Simon Callow – follows the Montignac 'French Diet' method.

■ Kenny Chesney – (the five-minute Renée Zellweger husband) sticks zealously to raw eggs, workouts and yoga.

■ Bill Clinton – shops around the diet lexicon; currently held to be in the grip of the GI craze.

■ Randy Jackson – *American Idol* judge had gastric bypass surgery and lost over 89lb (7st).

■ Aled Jones – lost nearly 2st (22lb to be exact) on *Strictly Come Dancing.*

■ Karl Lagerfeld – lost 89lb (7st) and then attacked British women for being too fat.

■ Brian McFadden – publicly taken in hand by Gillian McKeith and put on a no-beer GI diet.

■ Antony Worrall Thompson – liked the GI lifestyle so much he brought out his own book.

■ John Travolta – 'I love my food but worry about my weight and reluctantly go on diets from time to time.'

■ Robbie Williams – male yo-yo who's reputedly tried everything from exercise to diet pills.

HAZARDOUS WAIST?

In 1980, 6% of British men were considered obese, compared to 22% now. In all, 68.2% of British men are now classified as obese or overweight – compared to 58.9% of women. Also in 1980, there were more than two women dieters for every man trying to lose weight – now that ratio has shrunk to 1.7 female slimmers to every man. Mintel predicts that within 40 years the sexes will be trying to fight the flab side by side.

Only 32% of men say they diet to boost their self-esteem, compared to over half the women questioned. But men don't even like to say the 'D' word. 'Diet is a total no-no for our front cover,' said one national men's magazine editor. Men are more likely to cut out alcohol and ramp up the exercise than go for meal replacements, and prefer to talk of 'cutting back' or 'watching their weight' rather than actively 'dieting'. A man drinking two pints of beer a day will, over the week, drink a whole day's calorie allowance. Other main downfalls are curries and crisps.

Compared with 27% of women, 42% of men say being overweight doesn't bother them at all. Around half of men who are actually overweight consider themselves to be normal weight (totally the reverse of women) – fat men are much more likely to consider themselves physically attractive than plump women. However, men are more likely to be motivated to lose weight to help them 'chat someone up' (43%) than for health reasons (39%). A third of men questioned know there is a link between being overweight and erection problems.

An eDietsUK website survey found that almost half of their online dieters had felt pressured into losing weight by their 'pushy partners'. Nearly nine out of 10 men are against joining slimming clubs (some saying Marjorie Dawes, the bitchy diet leader from *Little Britain* has put the nail in the coffin of that idea). A fifth of

those who joined an online slimming programme instead said they were too embarrassed to tell anyone they were trying to lose weight. But in 2004, the runner-up in *Slimming* magazine's Slimmer of the Year competition was a man, Justin Larkin, who lost 98lb (7st). Mintel estimates that British men spent £827m in 2004 on grooming products, suggesting that there's a market to be tapped in male dieting products.

HAVE YOU NOTICED?

While there isn't anything like the same body fascism for men in Hollywood as there is for women, there is an unacknowledged link between fat and social standing. Have you noticed that although some TV shows do have paunchy actors – John Goodman, Tom Arnold, Drew Carey or Kevin James (from *The King of Queens*) – they are almost always when working-class or ethnic settings are meant to be conveyed?

TRAINING FARE

When Arsene Wenger became manager of Arsenal, one of the first things he did was to ban chips from his players' diets. But did he ban doughnuts, too? Gram on gram, chips contain a quarter of the fat of doughnuts.

FAT AND HAPPY

There is a strange link between obesity and depression which would seem to indicate that being fat actually makes otherwise depressive men happier. In a National Alcohol Survey, obesity was associated with a 37% increased risk of depression in women, but a 37% decreased risk of depression in men. There was a similar link between obesity, gender and suicide – with fat women at increased risk of suicide, fat men at less risk.

WEIGHTY WORDS

My advice if you insist on slimming: Eat as much as you like – just don't swallow it.

Harry Secombe

HE COULDA BEEN A CONTENDER

At a dinner with Marlon Brando, the President kicked off with a typical Kennedy needle.

'Marlon, have you gained weight? Looks like you put on a few.'

'Nary an ounce,' Marlon smiled through his pasta.

'Then the CIA sent up the wrong information,' the President grinned.

'And I'll bare-knuckle fight the man who says I have.' Marlon smote the table. 'I'll bet you I weigh less than you do, Mr President.'

'You're going to tell the President of the United States he's fatter than that?' said Kennedy, mock indignation. Laughter from the rest of us.

'I'm not saying it, I'm guaranteeing it. Where's a scale?' The large helping of pasta still had not cleared Marlon's throat, his words were muffled.

'Come on.' The President was out of his chair and heading to the bathroom. The rest of us followed.

'You first, Mr President.'

'Marlon, you're with friends. Don't be shy, get on that scale and face the music,' replied the President.

With urging from us, Marlon stepped on to the scale then set his fingertips on the tile trim to lift some of his weight. Like that, he weighed 187lb. Kennedy waved his empty hands as he got on the scale. He weighed 176lb.

'Get some food in this man,' Marlon said as we headed back to the living room. 'You can't lead a country on 176lb.'

From *Marlon Brando, The Naked Actor*

THE ADONIS COMPLEX

A recent study of 140 men showed that, when given images of muscular males advertising Calvin Klein and Emporio Armani underwear, more than 50% of them said they felt utterly intimidated. Whereas in past decades, advertisements tended to feature a non-threatening 'everyman', now the norm is for rippling muscles, brawny torsos and impressive six-packs. Now bulimia among men is on the rise – 100% in the last two decades. Of course, it doesn't help when beauty-and-brawns like David Beckham (Vodafone, Police etc) and Freddie Ljungberg (Calvin Klein) are the ones advertising... Even the most dedicated of gym-goers would be put in the shade. But we're still cross about the exercise/metabolism injustice so we're not going to feel too sorry for them.

MUMMY'S BOY

When Shane Warne failed a drugs test and was sent home from the cricket World Cup of 2003, he attributed his failure not to performance-enhancing drugs but to the diet pills sent out to him by his mum. Proof both that there are still mummy's boys – even at sport's highest level – and that if even macho Aussie men like Shane are using dieting to excuse their behaviour then the rest of you lardy boys better sit up and take notice.

RISE OF THE KEN DOLL

It's not just women who want plastic surgery – Transform, the UK's largest chain of cosmetic surgery clinics, estimates that 15% of all cosmetic procedures in Britain are now carried out on men. In America, there's been a huge increase in the number of men secretly having 'liposculpture', where fat is sucked out of the stomach and love handles, to give the appearance of six-pack abs.

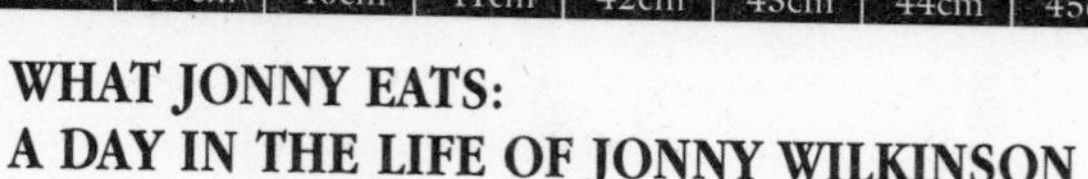

WHAT JONNY EATS:
A DAY IN THE LIFE OF JONNY WILKINSON

Breakfast: a bowl of porridge, an omelette made with six egg whites and three yolks, ham, mushrooms, wholemeal toast

Lunch: soup, chicken, stir-fry veg and salad, brown rice and a wholemeal roll

Dinner: fish with salad, jacket potato or a good, lean cut of meat

Evening snack: a flapjack, cottage cheese on toast, or beans on toast

Drinks: high-energy sports drink and a carbohydrate and protein-recovery drink plus 3-5 litres of water

TOTAL CALORIES: 4-5,000 calories

AVERAGE RECOMMENDED MALE CALORIE ALLOWANCE: 2,500 calories

DAVID – NOT SUCH A GOLIATH

He's always cited as the perfect specimen of manhood (except for the bit that was tucked under a marble vine leaf for much of the nineteenth century) but now Florence's most famous pin-up, Michelangelo's David, has been criticised by Pilates expert Alan Herdman for having love handles, bad posture and 'weight distribution that is all wrong'. Ah, how are the mighty fallen.

MEN IN MUD

Male-only spas are also booming: the Refinery, with two branches in London, has seen its client list rise from 1,500-2,000 in a year – alongside shaves and haircuts, slimming mud wraps are also increasingly chosen from the menu.

38cm | 39cm | 40cm | 41cm | 42cm | 43cm | 44cm | 45cm | 46cm | 47cm

MEN WHO PUBLICLY LOVED THE ATKINS DIET

Roman Abramovich

David Baddiel

Jack Black

Paul Burrell

Bob Geldof

Oliver Letwin MP

Francis Maude MP

Brad Pitt

Harvey Weinstein, Miramax boss

Dale Winton

MR SUPER SIZE ME

When Morgan Spurlock finished filming *Super Size Me*, his stinging critique of fast-food corporations, he had put on 25lb (1st 11lb), had off-the-scale cholesterol readings and a liver teetering on collapse. Billed as a 'stunt with a very serious message behind it' and by him as a 'really great bad idea', the film followed his descent into burger hell, mapping his experiences as a gorging guinea pig, eating nothing but McDonald's for 30 days to demonstrate the detrimental impact of a fast-food, low-exercise lifestyle. He later described it as 'a straight downhill slide to culinary boredom and intestinal suicide.' Then, in a strict regime imposed by his fiancée Alex, a vegan chef, he lost it all again. The bad news is that, even years on from the experience, those 30 days still haunt his body – 'the main thing that has stayed is my body's ability to put on weight,' he says. 'When you lose weight after gorging like that, those fat cells don't go away, they just get real skinny. They're still sitting inside you holding their fat buckets just waiting for an opportunity to fill them up again.'

THROUGH GRITTED TEETH: THE 'MEN ARE BETTER AT DIETING' CONTROVERSY

It pains us to report that, Johnny-come-latelies though they might be to the dieting world, research has suggested that men might be better at losing weight than women. The clubs, in their desperation to hook the lucrative men-dieter market with tempting statistics, may be clutching at straws because we all know that men join slimming clubs in only a tiny minority. But Slimming World research found that, in 12 weeks, 91% of men lost 5% of their body weight whereas in the same period, only 53% of women did the same. Not only that but, after 12 weeks, average weight losses among women were 15lb (just over 1st) whereas men lost 23.5lb (nearly 2st).

Dr Jacquie Lavin, nutritionist with Slimming World, has suggested several reasons for the difference but it makes depressing reading for women. Men tend to have a higher muscle mass, so burn up energy faster. Women who attended slimming clubs have often tried various diets over a long period of time and tend to be jaded about the chances of success. Men, on the other hand, are newer than women to the whole dieting concept and, once they've made the controversial decision to join a slimming club, are more likely to be less cynical and more motivated to follow instructions. We're tempted to wring our hands and say, give us a break, but slimming clubs are delighted, sniffing out the potentially profitable male sector and creating men-only support groups to rise to the expected demand.

WEIGHTY WORDS

To a man, offering him food is like offering him a breast.

Anon

EXTREMES AND CONTROVERSIES

The post-surgical Dolly Parton looks like the post-surgical Ivana Trump looks like the post-surgical Michael Jackson looks like the post-surgical Joan Rivers looks like… Barbie

MG Lord, *Forever Barbie*

In this chapter we go beyond the fatso to the so fat. We swing wildly from those who are fat beyond imagining to those who will put themselves through pain beyond imagining to achieve the appearance of slenderness. From porkers to plastic surgery, there will always be extremes of behaviour – and extreme lengths gone to by certain companies to capitalise on that consumption – and we've gone to all ends of the scale. So how much do we blame the world's most popular fast-food companies for fattening us up, or the likes of diet pills for spinning us impossible dreams or even something as banal as the city where we live? Then there is the bulging time bomb that is childhood obesity – once only an extreme, now increasingly the norm, with all the concomitant controversy on what we are going to do about it. It's all about record-breakers, wrinkle-breakers and bed-breakers.

Extreme obesity is not a modern phenomenon, it's just that it happens more often these days. Human beings have been getting spectacularly fat since prehistoric times, as shown by the generously bulging Venus of Willendorf, a statuette (thought to date 24,000-22,000BC) with spare tyres and bosoms that Dawn French would be proud of. Classical times were not short of fatties either: like Nichomachus of Smyrna, who was so heavy that he could neither move nor be moved from his bed. Or the Roman senator who was able to walk only when two slaves carried his belly for him, and the Egyptian pharaoh whose midriff was broader than the span of a man's outstretched arms.

A grand and erudite way of telling someone that they're a porker is to tease them about their Dionysian appetites. The original Dionysius of Heracleia was notorious for his appetite, and eventually grew so weighty that he could hardly move. He was said to have suffered from apnoea or narcolepsy as well, which made his doctors prick his flesh with needles when he fell asleep on his throne.

A contemporary poet quotes him saying that he aspired to end his days, 'on my back, lying on my many rolls of fat, scarcely uttering a word, taking laboured breaths, and eating my fill,' for of all the ways a man might die, an excess of luxury was the only truly happy death. In the end, he lived to what was then the ripe old age of 55, earning a reputation for fairness and generosity that competed with his size as an object of astonishment.

WEIGHTY WORDS

I'm anorexic really. Anorexic people look in the mirror and think they look fat. And so do I.

Jo Brand

I'm on a new diet – Viagra and prune juice. I don't know if I'm coming or going.

Rodney Dangerfield, *Only Fools and Horses*

If only it were as easy to banish hunger by rubbing the belly as it is to masturbate.

Diogenes

38cm 39cm 40cm 41cm 42cm 43cm 44cm 45cm 46cm 47cm

URBAN HEALTH MYTHS

■ The one where eating bananas from Costa Rica meant you ingested flesh-eating bacteria... sounds like just another diet fad to us.

■ The one where aspartame, the artificial sweetener, gave you multiple sclerosis, lupus and a variety of other ills. We don't need to know whether this is true to know that Diet Coke just isn't good for us.

■ The one where Taco Bell was allowed by the government to put mealworms into the beef products on the grounds that they were cheaper, less fatty and with less calories than pure beef.... Hmm, mealworms or ground-up cattle hooves and eyeballs? One is an urban myth, one is the probable reality. Rock and a hard place, we say.

■ The one where canola oil was not a foodstuff but an industrial by-product of rapeseed oil not originally intended for human consumption – and related to the use of mustard gas in the trench warfare of World War I. With much blustering on this one, better switch to sunflower oil anyway.

■ The one where microwaving foods in clingfilm gave you cancer – vociferously denied; even though there's evidence that there is some breakdown in the clingfilm's molecular structure, there's no evidence to link that to an incidence of cancer.

■ The one where Twinkies, the infamous American cake bar, was so stuffed with artificial preservatives that it had a shelf life of several decades... This one nearly put the Twinkies company out of business.

WEIGHTY WORDS

You never know where to look when eating a banana.

Peter Kay

PHENOMENAL FATSOS

The *Guinness Book of Records* always used to be the definitive source of information on the heaviest contemporary men and women. But in recent years, its annual list has been curtailed – perhaps the editors simply ran out of space for the sheer number of people trying to out-fat each other, or perhaps they got disgusted with the increasing exploitation of such individuals by diet centres and unscrupulous TV talk-show hosts, who meddle with super-heavyweights in the way that monarchs once needed court dwarfs. Here, then, is our list of the six heaviest people of the last hundred years. Read it and weep, not just for the poor souls abandoned to their beds but for the particular instances of bravery and, on the flip side, the total exploitation shown them.

Carol Yager (1960-1994) of Flint, Michigan; 5ft 7in, is estimated to have weighed more than 1,600lb at her peak, an incredible 114st 4lb. She had been fat since childhood but in 1993, aged 33, she was measured at 1,189lb (nearly 85st) when admitted to Hurley Medical Center, suffering from cellulitis. She lost nearly 500lb (over 35st) on a 1,200-calorie diet, but most of that weight was thought to be fluid, and she regained all of it and more soon after being discharged. Her teenage daughter, a boyfriend and a group of volunteers helped take care of her. Despite extravagant coverage by diet maven Richard Simmons and talk-show host Jerry Springer, Yager received little practical assistance in return for her media exposure (though Springer continues to profit from her appearance on his show, having rebroadcast that episode at least four times). She was refused further hospitalisation on the grounds that her condition was not critical, despite massive water retention and signs of incipient kidney failure, and died only a few weeks later, aged just 34.

Jon Brower Minnoch (1941-1983) of Bainbridge Island, WA; 6ft 1in, is estimated as weighing 'probably more than' 1,400lb (100st) in 1979, at which point it took 13 people just to roll him over in bed. Minnoch, like many of the heaviest people, suffered from massive oedema, water retention; his weight was augmented by at least 900lb of fluid at its peak. The former taxi driver had always been unusually heavy, but he claimed to have been in no way handicapped by his size until a 500-calorie diet sapped his muscle strength and left him at the brink of death. Subsequent hospitalisation brought him down to 476lb (a mere 34st) in 1981, mostly through the loss of 12-14lb of fluid per week. He was readmitted later that year after regaining 200lb (14st 4lb) in seven days. Although physicians at University Hospital in Seattle persisted in treating him with a 1,200-calorie diet, he weighed about 800lb (over 57st) at the time of his death. Other details of his physical condition were withheld from the press. Minnoch was the father of two children by his wife, Jeannette, who weighed in at a measly 8st.

Roselie Bradford (b. 1944) of Sellersville, Pennsylvania; 5ft 6in, weighed 1,053lb (75st 3lb), but estimates that she weighed more than 1,200lb (86st) at her peak two years earlier. Already over 300lb (21st 6lb) when she dropped out of college, Bradford. Incredibly, she became an exercise instructor, running seven miles (11.3km) three times a week, but continued her steady gain in weight. At 374lb (almost 27st) she underwent an intestinal bypass operation, which caused serious complications. She was back to 350lb (25st) when she married her husband Bob in 1973, reached 500lb (over 35st) after the birth of her son, and as her body grew, so did her appetite. After contracting septicaemia in the early 1980s, she spent most of the next decade in bed, eating as much as 15,000 calories per day: demolishing three large pizzas in 40 minutes, then tucking into dessert.

At her peak, she was 8ft wide, and took up two reinforced king-sized beds. Her bustline was over 100in, and her hips carried 200lb (14st 4lb) 'saddlebags' that hung down as far as her knees. 'People would visit me and sit on the bed, not realising they were sitting on part of me,' she recalled. When she fell out of bed, rescue workers used an inflatable cushion designed to right overturned cars to get her back into place. After being treated for symptoms of heart failure, she was eventually persuaded by American diet guru Richard Simmons to embark on a five-year diet, an experience she described as hellish. She nevertheless got down to under 300lb (21st 6lb), setting a world record for weight loss.

Michael Edelman (1964-1992) of Pomona, upstate New York; *Guinness* listed him at 994lb (71st), but his mother estimates that he weighed some 1,200lb (over 85st) at his heaviest. He had already reached 154lb (11st) at age seven, and left school at 10 because he could no longer fit into the desks. After that he spent most of his time in bed, or sharing massive meals with his 700lb (50st) mum. Michael liked to start the day with four bowls of cereal, toast, waffles, cake and a quart of soda, and end it with a whole pizza with the works for a bedtime snack. Mother and son tried every new diet that came along, 'but after a few days, we'd reward ourselves with a chocolate cake. Then we'd call for a pizza and that would be it.' When the two were evicted from their Wesley Hills home in 1988, Michael had to be moved by forklift. After his exposure in the press, dozens of hospitals and diet promoters vied to get him in a weight-loss programme, but Michael was determined to get thin on his own. He appeared in three different tabloids in one week when he publicly vowed to lose enough weight to consummate his relationship with 30st Brenda Burdle, but the couple grew apart when they both gained weight instead of losing it. After the sudden death of Walter Hudson (below), with whom he had formed a long-distance friendship, Michael developed a pathological fear of eating. He rapidly lost several hundred pounds, taking nourishment only when spoon-fed. At about 600lb (42st 12lb), he literally starved to death.

Walter Hudson (1944-1991) of Hempstead, New York; 5ft 10in, weighed in at 1,197lb (85½st – though the industrial scale broke in the process of weighing him). His chest was measured at 106in, his waist at 110in. Hudson was discovered by the press in 1987, when he became wedged in the door of his bedroom and had to be cut free by rescue workers. An agoraphobic, he'd spent most of the past 27

WEIGHTY WORDS

Diet is… the orderly, due course observed in the use of bodily nourishment for the preservation, recovery and continuance of the health of Mankind.

Thomas Moffett (1553-1604) English Renaissance scientist

The local groceries are all out of broccoli, loccoli.

Ray Blount

years in bed at home with his family, and gave every indication that he was content with both his weight and his situation. 'I just ate and enjoyed it.' Despite his massive size, *Newsday* reported that he was extraordinarily healthy: his heart, lungs and kidneys all functioned normally, while astonished doctors noted that his cholesterol and blood-sugar levels 'showed the chemistry of a healthy 21-year-old.' Many celebrities and diet promoters adopted Hudson as their cause cèlébre despite this healthy diagnosis, persuading him that losing weight was necessary to save his life. Activist-turned-nutritionist Dick Gregory used Hudson to promote his Bahamian Diet, and claimed that his protégé lost at least 200lb (14st 4lb) – sometimes claiming as much as 800lb (57st 2lb) – under his care (though *Newsday* noted that Hudson never seemed to look any thinner) but when Hudson refused to perform for the cameras on cue, Gregory summarily abandoned him. Hudson himself gave conflicting stories, sometimes claiming to weigh as little as 480lb (34st 4lb) or as much as 1,400lb (100st) and only allowed himself to be weighed once. He died in his sleep after years of intermittent starvation dieting, a few weeks after announcing wedding plans. His body was found to weigh 1,125lb (87st 5lb), and his massive coffin required 12 pall-bearers.

Francis John Lang, aka Michael Walker (b. 1934) of Gibsonton; 6ft 2in, claimed to have reached a maximum weight of 1,187lb (84st 11lb). Unlike the others on this list, Lang was not a fat child or teenager – he had weighed only 150lb (10st 10lb) as a soldier in Korea. He blamed his massive weight gain on prescription drug abuse, claiming that his narcotic of choice had the side effect of giving him an uncontrollable appetite. Though unable to walk (a handicap that kept more than one fat lady out of the side show), Lang found a unique way of capitalising on his situation: he had a mobile home built with observation windows, and travelled the country putting himself on display at carnivals and fairs. Lying nearly nude on an oversized circular bed, he preached to the curious about the evils of drugs, using his own body as the moral lesson. In early 1972, Lang was hospitalised in Houston for a suspected heart attack, at which time he was estimated to weigh between 900 and 1,000lb (64-71st), aged 38. His symptoms proved to be caused by an inflamed gall bladder, probably aggravated by his weight loss, and the examining physician declared his heart to be 'unusually normal'. By 1980, Lang had reportedly reduced to 369lb (26st 5lb).

SUCKING OUT THE FAT

In America, the number of cosmetic procedures more than doubled between 1997 and 2002 but even here in the UK we're becoming hooked on plastic surgery. According to the British Association of Aesthetic Plastic Surgeons, there was an 18% increase in the number of people having cosmetic surgery procedures in 2004 – mostly for 'body-contouring'. Liposuction remains the second most popular procedure in the UK after breast enlargement – and it is the most popular worldwide. Of all surgery performed, 90% was on women.

RIGHT ROYAL

One man who looks like a stripling next to the phenomenal fatsos above is the world's heaviest monarch, the infamous King Taufa'ahau Tupou IV of Tonga who weighed in at his country's only adequate scales, at the airport, in September 1976, at 462lb (33st). Beefiness ran in the Tongan royal family – the story goes that when the rotund Queen of Tonga attended a European coronation, she rode in a carriage with a slimmish young man who looked extremely nervous. 'Who's that young man with the Queen of Tonga?' asked one courtier. 'Her lunch,' replied another. King Taufa'ahau, however, was not going to take his 33st lying down: by 1985, he was reported to have slimmed down to 22st and, by 1998, had lost further weight as the result of a fitness programme.

STRANGEST DIET

Known popularly as Monsieur Mangetout (Mr Eat Everything), Michel Lotito took only certain aspects of the low-fat, high-fibre dieting gospel to heart, given that he has been eating mostly metal and glass since 1959. Gastroenterologists have described his ability to consume 2lb of metal each day as 'unique'. Michel says that health food staples bananas and hard-boiled eggs make him sick; he just likes to snack on the occasional jumbo jet.

DID YOU KNOW?

Vegetarians live longer and have more stamina than meat-eaters but they have a higher chance of getting blood disorders.

LAND OF PLENTY, PLENTY OF LARD

The following records were set in America. We shall say no more…

■ Largest apple pie ever baked weighed 34,438lb, in Washington DC – 16 August 1997

■ Largest bag of cookies measured nearly 11ft high and contained 100,152 President's Choice Decadent Choc Chip Cookies at the Loblaws Wonderland Market in Ontario, Canada – 6 September 2001

■ Largest bagel, weighing 714lb with a diameter of nearly 5ft, was blueberry flavour, and baked by Lender's Bagels of Ilinois – 23 July 1998

■ Largest bowl of pasta weighed 7,355lb and was made by *The Keeler Show* TV programme with Tony's Pizzeria, in Hartford, New York, on 14 February 2004 (for a different sort of Valentine's)

■ Largest box of chocolates contained 90,090 (how do they choose such numbers?) individual chocolates in a Frango Mint Chocolates box weighing 3,226lbs in Chicago, Illinois, on 14 November 2002

■ Largest burger, made of pure Montana beef, measured 24ft in diameter and weighed 6,040lb

■ Largest Caesar Salad proved that salad is not always the light option, at 5,460lb from the MetroTech Business Improvement District in Brooklyn, New York on 6 June 2001

■ Largest cake weighed 128,238lbs (including 16,029lb of icing) baked by residents of Fort Payne, Alabama, on 18 October 1989

■ Largest cooked breakfast was organised by the Cowboy Breakfast Foundation in San Antonio, Texas, for 18,941 people in one hour on 26 January 2001; handed out free, it included eggs, milk, tacos, sausage, coffee, fruit and juices – and actually fed 60,000 people over the course of the morning.

- Largest piece of toffee weighed 2,940lb and was created by Susie's South Forty Confections of Midland, Texas, on 17 September 2002 – it was made in the shape of Texas and contained a total of over seven million calories.
- Largest pizza order was filled by Little Caesar's for 13,386 pizzas for 40,160 employees of the VF Corporation of North Carolina, at 180 locations across the US, on 19 August 1998
- Largest spit roast was on 16 September 1973 when seven whole buffaloes, with a dressed weight of 3,755lb were impaled and cooked on a rotisserie 12ft long for 26 hours at Brisbane, California. We don't think Paul and Linda McCartney were invited…
- Largest wedding cake weighed 15,032lb and was made by Connecticut chefs for a New England bridal showcase on 8 February 2004
- Longest banana split was 4.55 miles long along the Market Street of Selinsgrove, Pennyslvania, on 30 April 1988
- And, finally, to put at rest the misconception that 'energy bars' were ever a real dieting option: the largest energy bar was a Circular Peak bar weighing 403lb, baked by a Colorado Springs baker on 20 June 1998.

WEIGHTY WORDS

I went into a McDonald's yesterday and said, 'I'd like some fries.' The girl at the counter said, 'Would you like fries with that?'

Jay Leno

A LIQUID LUNCH

No matter how many times we're told that alcohol – as the only calorie source that has absolutely no nutrients at all – is evil incarnate for slimmers, it hardly seems possible that it should be worse for us than traditional bugbears like chips, doughnuts or deep-fried Mars bars. The planet's biggest beer drinkers are, in a strange twist from all other world records of excessive consumption, not American. The Czech Republic is the leading beer consumer per capita with 35 gallons per person – nearly double that of the US. In 1998 – the most recent figures available – the Czechs as a whole consumed 436.7 million gallons of beer. Next round's on them, then.

ONLY SMARTIES HAVE THE ANSWER

In one of the more random records ever set, Kathryn Ratcliffe from Gateshead, Tyne and Wear, ate 138 Smarties in three minutes on 25 October 2003. Doesn't sound like that many? Well, she was obviously a slimmer in her other life, however unlikely that sounds – she picked up the Smarties with chopsticks.

WHAT A WAIST

Cathie Jung has been watching her waistline for years – but with rather more fervour than most. As someone who has been wearing a corset every day for the past 12 years, she is currently the world record holder for the smallest waist on a living person: 15in. Insisting that her corset-wearing habit has not caused her any health problems, Cathie admits to owning around 100 corsets, now wearing one for 24 hours a day.

Corsets haven't always just been popular with women – they were worn in ancient times by men from Crete who, over the years that they cinched themselves into the Ancient Greek equivalents, also permanently developed smaller waists.

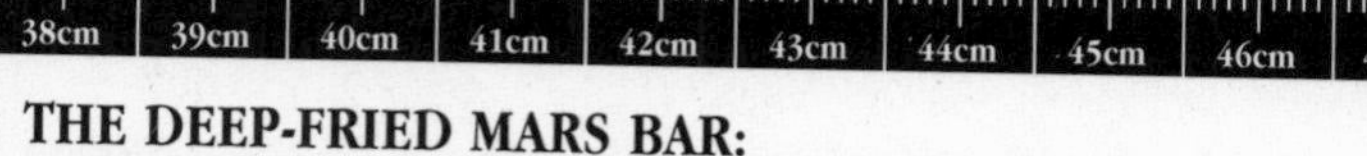

THE DEEP-FRIED MARS BAR: THE URBAN 'MYTH' THAT IS ALL TOO TRUE

- Almost a quarter of Scotland's fish and chip shops sell the deep-fried Mars bar.
- The craze started in 1995 in Stonehaven when local children asked if they could try Mars bars fried in batter.
- Now, of the 22% of chippies that sell them, 10 shops reported shifting between 50 and 200 per week; one in Stonehaven, its birthplace, sold 300 in one week.
- Calorie count of a Mars bar rises from 280 to 423 when it is deep-fried.

BEST-EVER APRIL FOOL FOR FATSOS

In 1994, full-page newspaper ads announced the 'New Biggest Ever Mars Bar'. The Emperor Mars Bar was 32lb of 'thick chocolate, glucose and milk' but it was 'on sale' for one day only: 1 April.

RED HERRING DAY

The world's oldest person, Hendrikje van Andel, was born in 1890 and ascribed longevity to her diet: 'I eat a herring and drink a glass of orange juice every day.' Is that it, Hendrikje? Blimey, we'd have died of boredom long before, if that was all we ate, every day.

RIGHT BACK AT YOU

There is a condition – luckily not widespread – known as emetophilia: sexual arousal in response to vomit or vomiting. Described in the *Archives of Sexual Behaviour*, in their 1982 article, 'Erotic Vomiting', as 'a previously unreported aberration' it has nothing to do with bulimia, that most private of eating disorders.

ADVOCATING AVOCADO

Most people don't even think of it as a fruit but the avocado is, in fact, the world's most nutritious fruit and has the most calorific value, at 163 kilocalories per edible 100g. Once derided as purely fattening, the avocado is now enjoying a comeback. Originally called 'ahuacatl' or 'testicle' by the Aztecs, it was celebrated as an aphrodisiac; then given a rave review by sixteenth-century Spanish historian, Fernandez de Oviedo; then used as a 'green midshipman's butter on biscuits' by the Royal Navy from c. 1700-1900. In the late 1960s and 1970s, the avocado became an increasingly common sight on aspirational dining tables but had to fight for its good name in the 1980s and 1990s when fat-finding calorie counters frowned on it. Finally, on the crest of the wave of 'good' fats, avocado oil is now enjoyed – and afforded – by the cognoscenti; and even ascetics like Rosemary Conley recommend it as a once-in-a-while healthy treat. And, no, that doesn't mean that you can rush out and enjoy that mayonnaisey avocado and prawn cocktail...

WEIGH TOO MUCH

Diet gurus recommend not weighing yourself more than once a week. Try telling that to Ray and Eileen Park of Noranda, Australia, who have a collection of more than 2,549 weighing scales, dating as far back as 1700.

BIG BUSINESS

Obesity is now a fat little money-spinner for gadget-makers in the US. New products include bathroom scales that go up to 1,000lb (71st 6lb), sponges on a stick to reach out-of-the-way folds of flab at bathtime, mechanical devices to pull on socks and cars with steering wheels realigned to make space for expanding guts.

38cm 39cm 40cm 41cm 42cm 43cm 44cm 45cm 46cm 47cm

BRITAIN'S FATTEST CITIES IN 2004

Taking into account consumption of fat and calories, drinking habits, incidence of heart disease, number of fast-food outlets – balanced against gym membership, availability of open spaces and the consumption of fruit and vegetables.

1. Manchester
2. Stoke on Trent
3. Liverpool & Swansea
5. Leicester
6. Glasgow
7. Edinburgh & Wolverhampton
9. Belfast
10. Nottingham
11. Bradford
12. Birmingham
13. Sheffield
14. Plymouth
15. Derby
16. Newcastle
17. Coventry
18. Bristol
19. Cardiff
20. Leeds
21. Southampton
22. London

GOING FOR GOLD

With high-protein shakes, complex carbs and the latest in dietary technology, today's athletes are the world's ultimate dieters. Yet incredibly, as recently as 60 years ago, the ideal recipe for Olympian success was thought to be sweets and chocolates. At the 1948 Olympic Games, although the British athletes were subject to strict post-war rationing, they were each given more than half a pound of sweets and/or chocolate a day, feeling that it would put them at a psychological advantage over their foreign counterparts.

BIG IS BEAUTIFUL

We may be brainwashed on a regular basis into thinking that the female ideal is the skinny pouting model we see in *Vogue*, but throughout history some men have just preferred the lady bountiful. In America, this preference has now, of course, been formalised into a movement: the Fat Admirers who loudly profess their love and admiration for BBWs – Big Beautiful Women. But now a bizarre sub-culture is taking things to dangerous extremes.

The TV programme *Fat Girls & Feeders* explored the crossing-of-the-line, whereby men – 'feeders' – no longer satisfied with a merely big partner, encourage and even coerce their women to gain weight to the point where the women become immobile. Feeders seem to enjoy the power they wield to make their companions submit to degradation: the excessive feeding, the helplessness of having to rely on the feeder for even the most basic human functions (washing, going to the toilet or just moving), and the fact that the 'fat girls' are trapped in their mountains of fat as effectively as in a cage. All these inhuman and cruel actions enhance the power of the feeder.

On the other hand, the women who allow themselves to be trapped in this helpless situation represent the ultimate need to submit. Having had to suffer the rejection and hostility of being obese for so much of their lives, they are so deprived of affection, so eager to please, so flattered by the attention they receive 24 hours a day, that they submit to having their lives totally perverted. In the programme, most of the 'fat girls' who were trapped by feeders eventually came to realise that they were being exploited in a most dangerous and deviant way. But often the 'fat girls' came dangerously close to dying as their systems were overwhelmed by the avalanche of fat that was being deposited in their bodies. Luckily, some of the women came to their senses and managed to 'escape' from their feeders then lose some weight with the aid of medical procedures.

'She seems to have put on a bit of weight in the build-up to the wedding.'

38cm | 39cm | 40cm | 41cm | 42cm | 43cm | 44cm | 45cm | 46cm | 47cm

IN THE DOCK: NINE THINGS YOU DIDN'T KNOW ABOUT MCDONALD'S

1. The 'M' of McDonald's famous golden arches is now more widely recognised than the Christian cross.

2. Today there are 50 million daily customers in 31,000 McDonald's outlets around the world – taking a record $3.9bn.

3. US citizens spent $110bn on fast food in 2000 – way more than any other country in the world – compared to a mere $6bn spent in 1970.

4. The McDonald's strawberry milkshake is said to contain a mixture of more than 30 chemicals.

5. Dr McKeith would be pleased: there are an average of 178 sesame seeds on a Big Mac bun, which makes it healthy, yes?

6. According to figures from the World Cancer Research Fund, the average burger has reputedly doubled in size since 1982.

7. The supposedly 'healthy meal' – Crispy Chicken Ranch Salad with croutons, dressing and a medium Diet Coke has 512 calories (over a quarter of a woman's daily recommended calorie allowance), 26g fat (nearly a whole day's fat allowance), 12g sugar (nearly two teaspoons) and 5.5g salt, (also blows a whole day's allowance).

8. Their cynicism in softening up the next generation of burger eaters knows no limits – McDonald's is the largest toy distributor in the world.

9. A Greenpeace-produced leaflet, *What's Wrong with McDonald's?* sparked a giant lawsuit against Greenpeace in 1990 – known as the McLibel case – which went on so long it ended up in the *Guinness Book of Records*.

THE NON-CHEWING MOVEMENT

In dire contrast to the Chewing Movement of the 1890s (see 'Chapter Two: Dieting through the ages') which advocated that each mouthful of food be chewed 32 times to aid digestion and weight loss, the world's fastest three course meal was eaten by Peter Dowdeswell of Earlsbarton, Northampton. In a paltry 45 seconds he downed a pint of oxtail soup, a pound of mashed potatoes, half a pound of tinned baked beans and sausage, followed by 50 prunes. Wonder why he needed the prunes…

DID YOU NOTICE?

Some unintentionally funny (but genuine) newspaper headlines:

- 'Milk drinkers are turning to powder'
- 'Giant tea bags protest'
- 'Golfers warned not to lick balls'
- 'Chef throws his heart into helping feed the needy'
- 'Diet of premature babies affects IQ'

38cm 39cm 40cm 41cm 42cm 43cm 44cm 45cm 46cm 47cm

IN THE DOCK: THINGS YOU DIDN'T KNOW ABOUT COCA-COLA

■ Each 500ml bottle contains 10 teaspoons of sugar.

■ Coca-Cola is the world's biggest brand, with 1.3 billion beverage servings every day.

■ Diet Coke has doubled in size in the UK, since launching here in 1983. Now 12 million Brits drink Diet Coke.

■ Iceland consumes more Coca-Cola per capita than any other nation.

THE VOICE OF A GENERATION

In a survey conducted for fave teen mag, *Bliss*, out of 2,000 teenage girls questioned, 70% disliked their faces, and 75% said that they would be 100% happier if they lost half a stone. Nine out of 10 were unhappy with their bodies with 67% saying that measuring up to 'perfect celebs' made chilling out about their bodyshapes even harder.

The Schools' Health Education Unit carried out a survey of 300,000 pupils in 2004 which found that almost half teenage girls regularly skipped meals in an attempt to lose weight.New figures show that one in 250 women in England and Wales suffer from anorexia (one in 2,000 males) while five times that number have bulimia (estimated: it's harder to detect). The National Institute for Clinical Excellence has described eating disorders as an 'epidemic'.

An 'epidemic of bone fractures' is now warned to be the worst-case scenario of teenagers following faddy, fat-free diets. Following a dramatic drop in the consumption of milk, cheese, yoghurt and eggs by nearly 75% of girls aged between 10 and 20, calcium levels are heading towards the dangerously low.

Hostility towards obesity is threaded throughout society but children have an especially extreme view. In a study of 10- and 11-year-old children, being asked which out of six line drawings of peer-aged children they liked best (one being 'normal' and five showing physical disabilities, one being overweight) nearly all put the fat child at the bottom of their preferences, below that of a child with a facial disfigurement. Between a quarter and a third of teenagers report being teased by peers for reasons of weight – with obese girls and thin boys suffering the most vicious mockery. Yet at the same time, one in 10 six-year-olds is obese and the total number of overweight children has doubled since 1982. We currently have the biggest problem of teenage obesity in Europe.

Children just love 'bad' foods. A study for the Consumers' Association in 2002 asked 246 children to keep a food diary. The average diet turned out to be like that of 'Lynne': sweet processed cereal for breakfast, peanut butter sandwiches and crisps for lunch and pizza for tea every day, washed down with Coca-Cola. In 2004, a three-year-old died from obesity-related heart failure.

Even after the Jamie Oliver campaign against Turkey Twizzlers, a petition with 300,000 angry signatures and the move from central government to remove them from school dinners, sales of the Twizzlers went up by a third in 2005.

OTHER END OF THE SCALE

The idea that 'thin is in' is a message being spread with evangelical zeal by a number of 'Pro Ana' or Pro Anorexia movement websites. While the rest of us wince and tut at skeletal pictures of Lindsay Lohan, Mary-Kate Olsen and Nicole Ritchie, there are people who find the painfully skinny celebs 'thinspirational'. The common thread of such websites – now banned by the main internet servers – is that anorexia nervosa is a lifestyle choice, with site names such as 'Dying to Be Thin', 'Starving for Perfection' and 'Stick Figures'. Some sound almost religious in their zeal with the 'Ten Commandments of Ana' with such rules as, 'Hunger hurts but starving works', 'Nothing tastes as good as thin feels', and 'You must buy clothes, cut your hair, take laxatives, starve yourself, do anything to make yourself look thinner – being thin is more important than being healthy.'

THE DUST DIET

One of history's most extreme dieters was the oddly named nun Julian of Norwich, who died in 1416. Voluntarily walled up in a cell attached to her local church, she lived off a slowly decreasing diet that eventually included dust itself.

EATING FOR LESS THAN ONE

Increasing numbers of British women are dieting during pregnancy, putting their unborn children at risk of serious illness in later life. Not only that, but the small minority of women who take slimming and thyroid pills during pregnancy are reputedly more likely to have gay children. Needless to say, this is an American phenomenon where 'undergaining' – practised by women who strive to gain less than the recommended 25-30lb (around 2st) during pregnancy – culminates in eighth-month elective Caesarians to avoid that inconvenient final few weeks' weight gain. The irony is that mothers-to-be who diet are putting their unborn children at risk of obesity in later life. When pregnant women diet, the metabolism of the growing foetus is permanently set to get by on less food. After birth, when the child is given normal amounts of food, this set metabolism accordingly stashes away more fat, leading to a tendency towards abnormal weight gain. So tuck in, Mum, eat for two, not less than one.

MAGIC LITTLE PILLS?

When ex-Guess model and billionaire-geriatric-marrying Anna Nicole Smith took to the catwalks, red carpets and television screens to boast about her weight loss through diet pill TRIMSPA, even the most jaded celeb-watchers had to be impressed. Gone was the balloon-like, slurring car crash of a person that had dominated tabloid headlines for the previous few years. Here was a perky, wasp-waisted, bright-eyed Anna Nicole. In a matter of months, she had lost a total of 70lb (5st) and attributed the weight loss to the diet pills made by her new employers, TRIMSPA. Sales of the pills rocketed and TRIMSPA can now be found in almost every US drugstore.

Anna Nicole took six pills a day, the full daily dose of TRIMSPA. But that wasn't all she took. She told the press she took a 'colon cleanser' laxative that kept her 'on the pot all the time' and had modified her diet, thereby admitting that it wasn't just the TRIMSPA pills that dropped the weight. So was this just another diet pill con? Well, yes and no. TRIMSPA contains hoodia gordonii, a plant native to South Africa, that has a long history of use as an appetite suppressant by the San indigenous peoples there, but it also contained a heap of junk: too much chromium, blood sugar-increasing glucosamine, food dyes and additives. Side effects could include anxiety, insomnia and migraines – and the pills were expensive, costing nearly £70 a month compared to the £13 a month you could spend on health shops' natural hoodia supplements.

38cm 39cm 40cm 41cm 42cm 43cm 44cm 45cm 46cm 47cm

STOP BEFORE YOU POP

Dr Ian Campbell of the National Obesity Foundation: "Very few over-the-counter diet pills are extensively researched or backed by credible clinical studies. If I gave dummy pills to 100 volunteers, some would lose weight as the placebo effect is very powerful."

- Consult a pharmacist rather than buying pills off the internet; they can advise about any interactions with medicines already being taken
- Avoid pills containing ephedra (also known as ma huang), a herbal stimulant linked to heart palpitations, high blood pressure and seizures.
- Beware chromium picolinate, a common slimming ingredient now believed to cause cancer
- Never take diet supplements for months on end; not enough is known about long-term effects and they are merely intended as an initial kickstart to a diet
- Never pin your hopes on a supplement; the inescapable and boring truth is that losing weight in the long term depends on lifestyle changes.

ALL IN THE NAME: THE FLABJAB

Astounding as it is that a product could be marketed under such a name, the Flabjab has generated excitement since seen on *Richard and Judy*. A mixture of lipolysis, lipomelt and lipostabil, the jab is derived from soy lecithin, which breaks down fat. Pictures on its website show double chins being miraculously jabbed away but results are mixed and the treatment expensive.

EXPERTS RATE 'MIRACLE' DIET PILL PRODUCTS

Adios: Doctor's Verdict: Terrible name, unsubstantiated claim to quicken up metabolism – we say 'adios' to Adios.

Anorex, Zantrex-3 and Xenadrine: Doctor's Verdict: Claims to speed up the destruction of immature fat cells and inhibit the production of new ones but, since they are only considered dietary supplements, it's doubtful they are as dramatic as they promise.

Bio-Trim: Doctor's Verdict: This is a no-no because of the chromium it contains.

CarboCurb: Doctor's Verdict: It's meant to inhibit the absorption of sugary and starchy food but the small effect it's been shown to have does not outweigh the psychological problems of the have-your-cake-and-eat-it approach.

Metasys: Doctor's Verdict: Contains green tea extract, which seems to help you burn fat as well as protect against cancer and heart disease so it's good for general health, no matter how effective or ineffective it is as weight control in the long term.

Reductil: prescription-only. Doctor's Verdict: Useful for those with morbid obesity as an appetite suppressant – as long as it is combined with a proper weight-reducing diet – but side effects can include an increase in heart rate.

Slender Silhouette: Doctor's Verdict: contains garcina, which suppresses appetite in animals, but the ill-advised concentration of guarana (three times as much caffeine as coffee) makes you twitchy and jittery.

Slim-Rite: Doctor's Verdict: Nothing recognised as a fat burner or appetite suppressant here and their size and smell make them hard to take.

Thermobol: Doctor's Verdict: Contains an interesting mix of fat-burners but the paltry amount of research evidence was far too short term.

Xenical: prescription-only: Doctor's Verdict: Works by preventing the absorption of ingested fat but side effects include flatulence and the dreaded 'anal leakage' for those consuming more than 40g fat per day and hoping to miraculously lose weight.

XLS Lipoclear: Doctor's Verdict: This shellfish-based fat-absorber is meant to eliminate fat in a 'natural' way, meaning less fat is available for absorption by your body. There's some truth to this theory, but who wants the diarrhoea that accompanies that 'natural' expulsion?

Zotrim: Doctor's Verdict: Can't see how it would, as claimed, slow the emptying of the stomach but if the makers have studies to prove that it does, that could indeed lead to weight loss – in tandem with some calorie control.

WEIGHTY WORDS

Krispy Kreme Doughnuts: Konsult Kardiologist.

David Letterman

'I can't see what's so scary about it,
but it sure made Mum scream.'

THE A-Z OF DIETS

**Stressed spelled backwards is desserts.
Coincidence? I think not!**

Anon

As Hillel Schwartz said in his book, *Never Satisfied: A Cultural History of Diets, Fantasies and Fat*, 'Diets seem to appear out of nowhere, in no time at all, like barbarians or wandering saints, and they seem to disappear as easily and swiftly as they come.' With about 5,000 diet books on the market and the knowledge that an estimated 12.5 million Brits are trying to diet, the sheer power of the dieting phenomenon can make the would-be dieter want to crawl back under the covers with only a family bag of Revels for company. But no matter how we sneer and snort at the next big thing in dieting, the newest red-hot regime that will rip off the pounds, there is always a little voice inside that bleats that this might be The One. That magical mirage of a moment when we can picture ourselves in that little black dress for the Christmas party, even if we're currently swamping around in the little black kaftan. Of all those women dieting, over 60% are on a specific programme carrying medical or celebrity endorsement. We are clearly desperate to believe. Which is why we have ridden to your rescue, to tame the dragon that is the diet industry and render it up to you in little bite-sized pieces.

On the menu, is a smorgasbord of proteins, carbs and some funny-tasting things in between. We have unashamedly veered towards the fashionable, with occasional dips into our dieting past and have, imaginatively enough, presented our dishes in an A-Z arrangement. Our own opinions are entirely subjective and are just our opinions.

A

ABS DIET by David Zinczenko

This is one for the men; 'The six-week plan to flatten your stomach and keep you lean for life' with macho touches to distract you from the girly topic of dieting: veggies described as Lean Green Machines, with the rocket sub-listed as 'the bone builder'. Recipes include Bodacious Brazilian Chicken and Ragin' Cajun Beans. At the core are the 'Abs Power 12' – a dozen foods whose initials spell out 'ABS DIET POWER' (Almonds, Beans, Spinach start the ball rolling).

We say: This could be entertaining were it not for the total lack of irony – and the requirement to eat six times a day *and* find time to work out at least four times a week makes it a tough one to maintain. ABSurd, we say.

ATKINS NEW REVOLUTION by Dr Robert Atkins

You can eat mountains of meat and fat but carbohydrates are the devil, so bring on the bacon and eggs, but wave bye-bye to pasta for ever. The science says that eating this way induces ketosis – a form of starvation where the body starts to feed on its own fat – yet you don't feel hungry. Fruit and vegetables are notable by their minor role in this revolutionary regime, exploding the usual sacred cows of dieting.

Celeb fans: Renée Zellweger (both times she had to shed her Bridget Jones weight), Jennifer Aniston, Brad Pitt, Geri Halliwell, Robbie Williams, Harvey Weinstein, Britney Spears

We say: Even before the horror stories of bad breath, kidney stones and rapid regain, this diet just felt all wrong, but some swear by it for dropping the pounds quickly and easily. Then the company went bust.

B

BEETROOT DIET

Boiled, liquidised, steamed, roasted, curried – any which way but loose for the little purple vegetable that leaves a big stain. Containing no fat, lots of fibre, lashings of foliate, potassium and manganese, the humble beetroot is a superfood that, on this plan, is eaten three times a day, with just 36 calories per 100g.

Celeb fans: The Warwickshire County Cricket club took the purple vow – and walked off with that year's County Championships with a game to spare. Apparently no one could, er, beet them.

We say: Even as fans of the root, we'll never become beetniks: the scary urine colour, messy preparation and its ability to stain anything – including, in some cases, teeth – just adds to the nutrition nonsense of rigidly promoting only one type of food. We like the opportunity to make bad puns, however.

BEVERLY HILLS DIET by Judy Mazel

This diet is all about timing. Specific foods are to be eaten at the same time or in a certain order each day. Fruit is always eaten by itself and protein should never be eaten with carbohydrates. This, apparently, prevents the storage of fat. In the first 10 days, only fruit is permitted. Then carbs are added and, on the nineteenth day, protein is finally allowed a look in.

We say: Textbook faddy, ridiculous, crash diet. Protein levels are dangerously low and several vitamins are missing. Side effects apparently include diarrhoea. One for anally-retentive, time-rich simpletons only.

B

BLOWOUT DIET by Dr Mark Mattson

Going against the theory of eating little and often, this headline-grabbing diet totes the idea that stop-start eating, as our hunter-gatherer ancestors used to do, is better for us than grazing.

We say: Certainly fits into the dining-out-with-mates lifestyle but the jury's still out as to whether this is a sustainable or healthy weight-loss approach.

BODY CLOCK DIET by Lyndel Costain

Shedding weight permanently depends on eating the correct foods at the right times. A rigorous approach to combining carbohydrates and proteins will reduce swings in blood glucose and hormone levels, making it easier to stick with the plan – a detailed 14-day menu, for starters, and the admonishment, should you cheat, to 'Stop what you are doing and step away from the food'. Yes, ma'am.

Celeb fans: Lisa Kudrow

We say: The bossy tone makes us want to stuff in a Crunchie when Costain isn't looking, but the recipes look tasty, if a little time-consuming to prepare.

WEIGHTY WORDS

I went to a conference for bulimics and anorexics. It was a nightmare. The bulimics ate the anorexics. But it was okay because they were back again in ten minutes.

Monica Piper

C

CABBAGE SOUP DIET

A rapid weight-loss plan in which you eat 'fat-burning' cabbage (and other veggies boiled to within an inch of their life) soup plus some other, very restricted foods including green veg, baked potatoes and fruit juice. Originally designed for recovering heart patients under very rigorous medical supervision, you can lose up to 15lb (just over 1st) in two weeks. No carbonated drinks allowed.

Celeb fans: Zoe Ball, Sarah Michelle Gellar, Joanna Lumley, Jilly Cooper, Jack Nicklaus

We say: The fat-burning theory is a myth; you smell of boiled cabbage, you fart like a cow and you faint after two days. But other than that, this one is just dandy for a crash diet!

COCONUT DIET by Cherie Calbom

Hugely successful in America, this posits that eating unrefined coconut oil will make your body burn fat faster and lower cholesterol since, far from being a dietary baddie, this virgin oil sparks a process called thermogenesis, thereby speeding the metabolism and thyroid function. Citing the South Pacific and Thailand as evidence, recipes like Thai Curry and cheese omelettes fried in coconut oil sound like outrageously undietary fare.

Celeb fans: Sting, Muhammad Ali

We say: The science is dubious at best on this one. We say it taps into the American obsession with allowable fat (Olestra, anyone?) and that despite the initially yummy recipes, coconut oil should stay in the sunscreen bottles.

D

DIET DIRECTIVES by Joan Breibart and Meredith Luce

The magic number here is 85 – but sadly it's not the number of pounds you stand to lose but the number of mouthfuls you are allowed to take – per day. The theory is that our stomach should only be the size of a 6in sausage and that, by pigging out, we've stretched it. By eating just 85 mouthfuls a day – balanced meals that can include the likes of pasta, steak, roast potatoes – we can re-shrink our stomachs in 21 days and thus put a cap on our food consumption.

We say: Might not work for wide-mouthed tree frogs. Or anyone with a short concentration span. Or, let's face it, anyone outside the circle of barmy Manhattanites keen on this diet, who clearly have nothing better to do than count how many mouthfuls they have in a day.

DR JOSHI'S HOLISTIC DETOX DIET

Stemming from Dr Joshi's Ayurvedic principles, you cut out all processed foods, dairy, wheat, alcohol, caffeine, sugar, red meat, nuts, shellfish, yeast, condiments and all fruit except bananas. And fill up on rice, beans, veg, juices and herbal teas. And the fun part is…?

Celeb fans: Kate Moss, Cate Blanchett, Gwyneth Paltrow, Juliette Binoche, Sadie Frost, Patsy Kensit

We say: One for Buddhist monks, celebs and hermits. Because the rest of us then go back to living in the real world and pile it all back on again.

E

EAT RIGHT 4 YOUR TYPE

Your blood type determines your way of digestion and therefore your weight, so if you are blood group A you need a different diet from someone who is blood group B. For example, blood type O should cut out carbs and dairy products and blood type A should be mostly vegetarian.

Celeb fans: Martine McCutcheon, Alicia Silverstone, Demi Moore, Liz Hurley (she said it sounded like nonsense but that she successfully lost weight)

We say: Scientifically unproven – and boring that you need to go and have a blood test.

F

F PLAN DIET by Audrey Eyton

This was 'The diet of the 1980s', and still selling – almost a million copies to date – which worshipped at the altar of fibre, hence the 'F'. Simple carbohydrates such as, most famously, baked beans and baked potatoes, fill the stomach and reduce the desire to overeat. Eyton's loving advocacy of beans, beans and more beans meant the 'F' for F Plan soon came to stand for the flatulence that resulted from it. Reissued as the *Complete F Plan Diet* in 1990, which brought in a new decade's worth of fans.

We say: Seems rather dull and monotonous. And we just can't get past the 'F' part and the thought of trying to work in an office with a permanent buttock clench to avoid being sniffed out.

F

FACE-READING DIET by Elizabeth Gray Gibaud

Devised by a naturopath at the Hay Clinic, this uses Chinese facial analysis, looking at the shape of your face, skin, eyes and hair to work out which foods you can and cannot eat. What follows is a customised detox plan, following basic principles of wholefoods and low fats (fruit is banned for having too much sugar).

Celeb fans: Kate Winslet, Cherie Blair

We say: We've heard of the eyes being the windows of the soul but this seems ridiculous. Better to have the Hip-Reading Diet which would at least be in the right ball park. But some nutritionists insist that everything from greasy skin and a pale complexion to bags under the eyes are all messages of nutritional deficiencies so perhaps we stand corrected.

FAT FLUSH DIET

Every three hours you eat certain foods that rev up your metabolism, including fruit, eggs and lean meat, plus cranberry water and a 'long life' cocktail. A low-carb detox plan that is very low in sugars.

Celeb fans: Halle Berry

We say: We were so encouraged by the title that the high-maintenance reality rather brought us back to earth with a bump.

WEIGHTY WORDS

Everything you see I owe to spaghetti.

Sophia Loren

F

FIT PACT PROGRAMME by Professor Ben Fletcher and team
'The psychological equivalent of the exercise bicycle for the human habit machine.' Right, then. FIT isn't fit, it's the Framework for Internal Transformation – aka the Do Something Different Diet. It means making small changes to your daily routine, breaking bad habits and disrupting behavioural patterns that cause you to put on weight.

We say: This one is still in trials, designed to help overweight children whose bad habits are not yet so ingrained. With that kind of game plan, we can only give it our full support, but it does all sound like the common sense that we 'grown-ups' secretly already know.

FOOD DOCTOR EVERYDAY DIET by Ian Marber
Hunger is the enemy, so avoid the body going into starvation mode with five meals a day suited to your personal metabolic type and predicated on the food-combining approach. Starts with a strict seven-day diet to improve digestion so that your system is able to shed weight more easily – and thereafter relaxes. The usual star players of nuts, seeds, oily fish, avocadoes and green veg take pole position but meat, wheat and other baddies are allowed. Oatcakes and rye bread are just two of the sanctioned snacks.

Celeb fans: Donna Air, Denise van Outen, Lisa B

We say: A remarkably unbossy diet which allows you the 80:20 rule of being good 80% of the time and doesn't dictate cutting out any foods. Nor does it flog any one diet theme to death. Easy to combine with yours and others' real lives.

F

THE FRENCH DIET by Michel Montignac

One of the fore-runners of the GI Diet, this no-calorie-counting diet is based on the inescapable fact that the French have the lowest body weight per capita and yet eat fabulously well, not only because of the foods they choose but the way in which the fresh ingredients are combined. Now it's been rejigged to embrace the glycaemic index… but still with its Gallic love of wine and food; some might find the amount of food preparation daunting.

Celeb fans: Nigel Lawson, Kylie Minogue, Jodie Kidd

We say: One word describes the success and appeal of this diet: wine. You're allowed it. Which makes it almost unique in the diet lexicon, and therefore we raise a glass to it. As it were.

G

GI DIET by Rick Gallop

Sadly not a US-military style diet aided by hot-blooded American soldiers, but the renaissance of the glycaemic index (GI), calculating what you are eating according to how fast the body converts that food into glucose for energy. By eating foods that break down slowly (such as apples) rather than those that break down fast (such as white bread and, strangely, watermelon) you can stabilise your blood sugar levels and lose weight. 'The more food is processed beyond its natural state the less processing your body has to do to digest it,' says Rick Gallop. 'The quicker you digest your food, the sooner you'll feel hungry again and the more you'll tend to eat.'

G

Celeb fans: Kim Cattrall, Kylie Minogue, Dannii Minogue, Natalie Imbruglia, Naomi Campbell

We say: The usual maxims about good and bad foods don't always apply here (watermelon is worse than crisps?) so close attention to the various tables will be needed in the early days. But it's not overly restrictive and the sheer ubiquity of it helps adherence – Tesco now labels blue, yellow, pink.

GRAPEFRUIT DIET

Grapefruits, we are told, contain fat-busting enzymes, so you are urged to eat a half before each meal to stay thin. Oh, and only eat 800 calories a day, with lots of 'metabolism-busting' caffeine and small portions of egg, dry toast and sometimes meat or fish. Ooh, tempt me.

We say: The phrase, 'she looked like she sucks on lemons' was never a kind description, which rather fits the mirage of the 'fat-busting enzyme'. It's all madness and let's not even go there.

WEIGHTY WORDS

Overheard in Harrods, 'Richard was very depressed. He thought he'd lost weight but when he got on the scales this morning he found it was only wishful shrinking'.

'Observer' in *Financial Times*

I often take exercise. Why only yesterday, I had breakfast in bed.

Oscar Wilde

G

GREAT AMERICAN DETOX DIET by Alex Jamieson

This is the one Mr Super Size Me did. When Morgan Spurlock ate nothing but fast food for a month for his prize-winning documentary, his girlfriend was waiting in the wings with a diet to get him back in shape. Within eight weeks he had lost 10lb and his liver function, blood pressure and cholesterol had all reverted to their original levels. Designed as a holistic approach to weight loss, energy levels and allergy elimination, there are eight weekly steps to total detox, breaking various habits along the way so that even when the regime is over, you may have retrained your body permanently – like no longer confusing thirst with hunger.

We say: Obscure health food ingredients, complicated water filtration systems and lengthy food preparations may make this seem daunting but as a time-specific campaign to clean up our act it gets our vote.

H

HAMPTONS DIET by Dr Fred Pescatore

Post Atkins, post South Beach Diet for jaded Manhattanites, based on the produce found in New York's weekend retreat. Blends low-carb living, whole foods and the flavours of Mediterranean cooking to include only good fats, like macadamia nut oil.

Celeb fans: Barbra Streisand, Steven Spielberg

We say: Glamorous and healthy – if we can't 'summer in the Hamptons, darling' we'd quite like to eat like we do. Not a penny-pincher's option, however.

H

HAY DIET

One rule: don't mix carbs and proteins in the same meal. The science is the body can't break down both at the same time, which causes it instead to store sugars as fat. So no meat and potato combos.

Celeb fans: Liz Hurley, Minnie Driver, Sarah Michelle Gellar

We say: It looks quite forgiving next to the Atkins Diet, but the method is more complicated than at first glance. All seems too much like hard work – and the health factor is questionable.

I

I CAN MAKE YOU THIN by Paul McKenna

It's not what you eat, but what you think. Using his NLP system (Neuro-Linguistic Programming) McKenna promises to change how you feel about food on a deep, unconscious level. Your cravings are curbed, you stop overeating and feel motivated to exercise.

Celeb fans: Kirsty Young

We say: We just can't help thinking of *Little Britain*'s 'Look Into My Eyes' when we consider this approach. Definitely one for those with time on their hands but not a rival to conventional diets.

WEIGHTY WORDS

Diet Coke with lemon – didn't that used to be called Pledge?

Jay Leno

M

MACROBIOTIC DIET

Part of a holistic approach to health – no red meat, raw veggies, a hill of beans and wholegrains, eating small meals often and chewing exhaustively. Critics claim a lack of first-class proteins (from meat and fish) and essential fatty acids. Caffeine, alcohol, bread and pasta are just plain banned.

Celeb fans: Gwyneth Paltrow, Madonna, Stella McCartney

We say: It's no real surprise that the celebrities attached to the macrobiotic lifestyle are those who, clearly, have a strong will and iron-clad self-discipline. Wouldn't we all be thin and healthy if we could all say the same? It's all too extreme and intolerant.

MARS AND VENUS DIET & EXERCISE SOLUTION by John Gray

Eating gender-specific foods will put the va-va-voom back into the bedroom – and have you losing 4lb a week into the bargain. It's all about When Dopamine Met Seratonin – men need high levels of the former hormone, women the latter. Either eat Gray's Mars Venus Super Shakes for men and women or stick to foods that pep up your hormones. For men, dopamine boosters include cottage cheese, salmon and steak; for women, low-GI carbs like porridge oats, sweet potatoes and a wagonload of fruits.

We say: Selling a diet on the promise that your sex life will improve is a cunning wheeze. Oh, and the diet's not bad either. Tedious preparing his 'n' hers meals, however.

M

MY BIG FAT GREEK DIET by Dr Nick Yphantides

Put away those visions of feta cheese, garlicky hummus and dripping lamb roasts. Instead apply your mind to the Seven Pillars of Weight Loss. In a nutshell, you have to alter your perception, stop eating for emotional reasons, start knowing when you are full, start exercising more and, oh, basically start a new life. Sounds like a cinch? Thought so.

We say: Great title – shame about the waffle inside. Dr Nick's own history might inspire you, however: for a self-confessed fattie who once broke a restaurant chair, he now looks happily fit.

N

NO CARBS AFTER 5PM DIET by Joanna Hall

Tough one to explain, this one. Amazingly, Hall proceeds to do so for 271 pages. It's all to do with digestion and creating a 'calorie gap' between the number of calories consumed and the number burned off. Actual choice of food is left to the individual.

Celeb fans: Dido, Michelle Collins

We say: Any diet that makes it nigh impossible to go out in the evening is for January dieters only. And recent research has finally debunked the perennial notion that eating late at night will make you fat.

N

NO-GRAIN DIET by Dr Joseph Mercola

An exclusion diet, that cuts out grains, starches and sweets. So far, so predictable but, should you feel tempted to stray, Mercola (complete with cringe-making self-portraits) advocates the Emotional Freedom Technique: tapping yourself on certain points over the face and body to relieve food cravings.

Celeb fans: Winona Ryder, *Friends* star Matthew Perry

We say: Mercola says the Emotional Freedom Technique is therapeutic acupuncture: we say that hitting ourselves doesn't feel like the positive mindset we want from a diet.

ONE MEAL A DAY

Not quite as drastic as it sounds, this regime calls for nibbling two small meals – in Liz Hurley's case, six raisins counts as one of those meals – and only having one regular meal, preferably at lunchtime. The theory goes back to the hunter-gatherers who had one blowout before and after a long hunting trip, while the womenfolk poked around for nuts, fruits and seeds at home; so a lot of its fans are men. The modern science of it is that if you give your system a rest, you are not pumping insulin out all day and you don't therefore lay down as much fat.

Celeb fans: Courteney Cox Arquette apparently shed the baby weight on this. Prince Charles, Liz Hurley, the forever sprightly Des O'Connor, recent father at 72, and that other Peter Pan, Cliff Richard

O

We say: Maybe good as a kickstart but not healthy in the long term for young people requiring calories for energy and concentration. Psychologically, focussing on one single meal is far more likely to create a worrying obsession with food.

P

PERFECT FIT DIET by Dr Lisa Sanders
Each of us is different and a regime that works for one person may not work for another. After looking at 700 diets and the last decade of huge dietetic discoveries, Sanders decided that everyone must have their own. The book answers exhaustive questions, leading to a medical, psychological and lifestyle profile – and a diet category that's right for you, from Counting Carbohydrates if you love meat and cheese to Counting Fats if you crave bread and pasta.

We say: There's something irresistible about filling out a quiz, but this book works better as a curiosity exercise than a lifestyle choice.

WEIGHTY WORDS

I personally stay away from natural foods. At my age, I need all the preservatives I can get.

the late George Burns

Men like to barbecue. Men like to cook only if danger is involved.

Rita Rudner

P

PERRICONE PROMISE by Dr Nicholas Perricone

This fishy one is also known as the Facelift Diet. Eat salmon three times a day to benefit from essential fatty acids, stimulating nerve function, 'plumping out' skin to improve facial sagging and wrinkles and, yes, losing weight. Improvements are promised from a three-day programme, followed up by a 28-day regime of fish, fish, fish, some leafy vegetables and a 'rainbow' of colourful foods like red peppers, oranges, yellow sweet potatoes, green beans, blueberries, indigo plums and violet aubergines. Then there's the stinger: supplement pills, which cost £199 per month.

Celeb fans: Courteney Cox Arquette, Jennifer Lopez, Bruce Willis, Heidi Klum

We say: Yeah, yeah, we already know how good oily fish is for us. But three times a day? We say the costly pills and expensive dry-cleaning bills on curtains and clothes after cooking fish all day, every day, make anything longer than the three-day programme untenable.

WEIGHTY WORDS

Self-contemplation is a curse, That makes an old confusion worse. He who himself begins to loathe, Grows sick in flesh and spirit both.

Theodore Roethke

But at the end of the day, 'Remember, there were people on the *Titanic* who turned down the sweet trolley'.

Jonathan Ross

R

RATION BOOK DIET by Mike Brown, Carol Harris and CJ Jackson
Back in the days when lean cuisine was an imperative not a 1970s lifestyle choice, the wartime diet depended on wholesome, home-cooked food. A cross between a recipe book and a trip down memory lane, the book aims to give sound nutritional advice rather than a prescriptive diet plan, peppered with quotes from WWII's *Ministry of Food's War Cookery* literature. Dandelion salad anyone? Some old favourites come with a modern twist: like corned beef and chilli rosti.

We say: Endearingly eccentric wartime nostalgia – but where's the powdered egg and the handsome GI Joe?

RAW FOOD DIET
As simple as it says on the tin. All you do is substitute at least one cooked meal for a raw one per day, but more if you can, since devotees believe that, when cooked, chemical changes destroy vitamins and enzymes that are vital for digestion and energy. Carpaccio and sushi count so it's not just rabbit food – and you can even, if you're desperate, eat rice; by soaking it for a few days.

Celeb fans: Sarah Jessica Parker, Natalie Portman, Uma Thurman, Demi Moore, Daryl Hannah, Donna Karan. David Wolfe, high priest of American veganism, even claimed that his penis got bigger on the Raw Food Diet…

We say: Closer inspection of this diet improves the initial celeb hippy association but while it's undoubtedly healthy, the slimming potential is limited. Raw food contains more water so it is more filling – and the increased chewing helps regulate the appetite, but that's about it.

R

REPROGRAMMING THE OVERWEIGHT MIND by Kelly Burtis
Thought control over the 'human machine' is the key to weight loss in this book, with chapters like 'Subconscious Perspective & Empowering Questions' and subheadings like 'My Love Goals'.

We say: Oh, reprogramming our mind sounded so promising… but even with the brain ache needed to read this, actual weight loss looks unlikely. Patronising psychobabble, best avoided.

S

SLIM-FAST
No counting, no complications and it's easy because you eat frequently – up to six times a day – on low-GI foods or shakes. Thereby a steady energy is maintained all day, forestalling blood-sugar crashes and weakening of resolve.

Celeb fans: Jordan, Whoopi Goldberg was an advocate until she was dropped by makers Unilever for making anti-Bush remarks

We say: They just can't make those shakes tempting. They just can't. And there's something awfully naff about being seen drinking a Slim-Fast shake. Sorry, Slim-Fast.

WEIGHTY WORDS

A man is in general better pleased when he has a good dinner upon his table, than when his wife talks Greek.

Samuel Johnson

S

SOUTH BEACH DIET by Dr Arthur Agatston

Along with the GI Plan, this Miami-originated scheme is the new contender to the throne vacated by Atkins. 'Sounds so good you want to eat it first… and then go there' said one reviewer. You stop eating bread, pasta, potatoes, ice-cream and sugar but can stuff yourself with bacon, cheese and steak. So far, so Atkins, but unlike that, you're encouraged to combine with copious fruit and veg. No alcohol allowed. Promises weight loss of up to 13lb (just under a stone) in two weeks (critics claim this is water, not fat).

Celeb fans: Nicole Kidman, Bette Midler, Bill Clinton, Hillary Clinton, Jessica Simpson

We say: Sounds too similar to stinky-breathed Atkins to hold our attention – or hold off the weight – but it's a big hit in America. The news that Kraft (maker of CheezWhiz dips, Oreo cookies and Toblerone) made a deal with Agatston to carry the South Beach 'seal of approval' on 200 of its product lines rather knocks its credibility.

SUGAR ADDICTS' DIET by Nicki Waterman

Calm down in the back there, no, you're not allowed back-to-back chocolates and biscuits. Despite the title, addicts are told to 'just say no' to sugar in any form, so look for the sweet stuff in vain in any of the recipes. As an ex 'sugar junkie' herself, Waterman rails against the 'cocaine of the food industry', blaming it for virtually all bodily ills: cancer, acne, depression.

Celeb fans: Sharon Stone

We say: Ah, the righteousness of the convert. How tedious.

T

THREE-HOUR DIET by Jorge Cruise

If you leave more than 180 minutes between meals, your body activates the 'starvation protection mechanism'. The body senses 'oncoming famine' and starts to store up fat. There are no bad foods, only bad portion sizes.

We say: Only in America could a three-hour gap without food be seen as impending famine. And the eating plan is insane: an Egg McMuffin for breakfast? Puh-leeeze.

TRAFFIC LIGHT DIET by Judith Willis

It's the GI Plan for people who are so busy driving to work they don't have time to figure out a diet plan. So Willis does it for you: taking the diet back to basics: 'green' foods are good, amber ones are for treats, foods on the red list should be avoided. The 'fun' comes from spotting the strange ones in each category: halibut is a green food, but trout is amber and whitebait is red. Go figure.

We say: Dieting for people who can't read? Or a catchy way to remember your dos and don'ts?

WEIGHTY WORDS

Dieting: A system of starving yourself to death so you can live a little longer.

Jan Murray

U

ULTIMATE NEW YORK BODY PLAN by David Kirsch

This is one for the quick-fix Manhattanites – its promise is that you don't need liposuction – just two weeks' hard effort. It's tough stuff indeed: a very low-carb, prescriptive ABCDEF diet – no Alcohol, no Bread, no Complex Carbs, no Dairy, no Extra sweets, no Fat or fruit – and 60-90 minutes of hard workout every day.

Celeb fans: Liv Tyler and Heidi Klum are just two of the yummy mummies trained by Kirsch

We say: As a way of getting into that little black dress, it's unarguable but just don't think you'll be thinking about anything else during those two weeks.

ULTIMATE WEIGHT SOLUTION by Dr Philip McGraw

Classic American approach – scary cover (Dr Phil clenching his fist with rictus grin) and boot-camp sergeant-major style intimidation: 'You have to get real about fat or stay real fat'. A '7 Key' approach launches you on an action-oriented and exhaustively detailed plan with which, Dr Phil says, 80% of his clients have not only lost weight but kept it off.

We say: Time-consumingly detailed and boomingly written, this is more hand-holding than we have the time or attention span for but the mooted success rate is impressive.

WEIGHT WATCHERS

Now over 40 years old, the grande dame of all slimming programmes. Run on a strict points premise – foods are given a 'points value' rather than measured in calories – the programme centres on the weekly meetings where a supervised weigh-in and discussion is the form. Group support helps you to stick on the path of achieving and maintaining your target weight.

Celeb fans: Claire Sweeney, Duchess of York, Drew Barrymore, Alicia Silverstone

We say: If you can face the group support/public humiliation, this tried-and-tested clear winner produces lasting, achievable weight loss.

X-FACTOR DIET

The X factor here is a recently discovered precursor of diabetes, a group of metabolic disorders known as Syndrome X, which has spawned the current tidal wave of obesity in the States and in Britain. Nothing to do with overeating and lack of exercise, then. Fight the tide with the usual low-carb diet of plants, proteins and oily fish fats: the aim is to defeat the insulin-resistance syndrome, limiting carbs and controlling blood sugar levels. All very scientific with diet options like 'Ketogenics' offered.

We say: Call us un-American but pizza sauce poured over tofu strips? Protein ice-cream? More than a whiff of desperation to catch the diamond-shaped fatties' interest, we think.

Y

YOU ARE WHAT YOU EAT by Dr Gillian McKeith

Blue-green algae, quinoa, miso soup and aduki beans are on the menu on this macrobiotic mishmash. 'Living Food Energy' – the actual powers of certain foods – is McKeith's mantra, along with an infamous obsession with cracked tongues and stools (not the three-legged variety). No red meat, eggs, dairy or bread (and obviously no alcohol) make this a tough one to get excited about: after a while, everything starts to look brown and sludgy.

Celeb fans: Michelle McManus has, so we are told, lost 70lb (5st) under McKeith's tutelage. Brian McFadden was her male pin-up when she helped him shed some weight.

We say: 1.5 million copies sold in the UK alone, alongside a strangely compulsive TV series have made Dr Gillian McKeith one to watch.

Z

THE ZONE by Dr Barry Sears

Regimented food-combining – each day you must eat 40% carbs, 30% protein and 30% fat – with a daily calorie count of 1,000 spread over five meals a day makes for a tough regime.

Celeb fans: Jennifer Aniston (switched from Atkins to the Zone, but she opted for the expensive meal-delivery option), Madonna, Janet Jackson, Sandra Bullock, pre-bulk-up Matt LeBlanc

We say: Not being very good at our arithmetic, the thought of having to work out a food ratio of 40:30:30 scares the bejaysus out of us – and 1,000 calories a day sounds like a fast train to Hungerland.

'How many calories are you?'

BEYOND THE HEADLINES

I've been on the Slim-Fast diet. For breakfast, you have a shake. For lunch, you have a shake. For dinner, you kill anyone with food on their plate

Rosie O'Donnell

The fame of medically or celebrity endorsed diets cannot be over-estimated: one survey in 2004 showed that more people had heard of the Atkins Diet than knew who Gordon Brown was. Pick up any magazine or newspaper – especially in the 'peak' dieting months of January ('New Year, New You!'), June ('Slimming Time for Summertime!') and November (Get Fat-free in time for the Festivities!') and that week's Hot New Diet will seem like the only answer. But what's the whole context? Is it fair that, in the slimming world, potatoes are now more villainous than Cruella de Vil? How many times do we have to eat aduki beans before we get to like the taste? And which foods are good for you no matter which celebrity claims to be nibbling them?

Stand aside while we impartial analysts, resplendent in our white coats, march before you in our serried ranks. In this chapter, we extract the fat from the fatuous and replace the eat (or ate!) in great to bring you the truth beyond the headlining diets. Oh, and if you read this chapter out loud to yourself, you will lose no less than 220 calories, no matter which diet you're on.

Are we not good to you?

THE NO-DIET DIET

The problem at the heart of most diets is willpower – just telling yourself to stop raiding the biscuit tin or scoffing crisps and eat healthily instead – and it is the reason why 95% of slimmers who rely on willpower to lose weight pile the pounds back on within a year. Now some university lecturers have come up with the Fit Pact Programme, known as the 'no-diet diet', which works by making you fill your time with simple tasks that you'd never normally do, claiming that switching off the TV and going to the theatre could actually help you lose weight.

The theory is that, because all diets focus on food, the thing you're trying to avoid is the very thing they're making you think about. So we have to remove ourselves both from the obsession with dieting and with the circumstances that make us think about foods: all those entrenched bad habits like the snacks you munch in front of the telly or the office pack of HobNobs you crave at that low time of 4pm. After four weeks of living life the Fit Pact way – as long as you follow closely and really choose the options that are most different to what you would do normally – you should have fallen into healthier habits naturally and broken the pattern of your bad eating habits.

BLAME IT ON THE BOOGIE!

Naturalists already knew that termites are affected by music: they will eat your house twice as fast if you play loud music. Now the *Journal of Applied Social Psychology* says that, like termites, women exposed to annoying loud sounds are more likely to binge on fast food than men. Apparently even constant background noise like the television or the radio can make you eat bigger portions faster. So let's put in those earplugs and settle down to a quiet life of uninterrupted weight loss. Excellent.

SOME ITEMS ON THE FIT-PACT PROGRAMME TASK LIST:

- Make a list of your childhood dreams
- Estimate your weight in five years' time
- Turn your mobile phone off for a day
- Listen to a different type of music
- See a play at the theatre
- Stop watching TV for a day
- Do some charity work – choose any local group
- Take a 15-minute walk after work
- Sing in the bath
- Play a child's game
- Go to the cinema on your own
- Listen to a bore
- Paint or draw in any medium
- Go to bed one hour earlier than usual
- Visit any local museum or exhibition
- Dance for two minutes alone
- Be nice to someone you don't like
- Write a story on any subject, of any length
- Go and talk to a neighbour

A HANDY LIST OF SUPERFOODS AND WHERE TO FIND VITAMINS AND MINERALS IN THE FOOD CHAIN

Avocados are the planet's most nutritious food, according to the *Guinness Book of Records*, at 163kCals per edible 100g. They might seem fattening at that calorie count, but have no cholesterol and are packed with vitamin A (healthy skin, hair and bones), vitamin B1, B2 and niacin (vital for creating energy), potassium (60% more than bananas and vital for clear thinking and stopping water retention), vitamin C and vitamin E (boosts energy levels and immune system).

Bananas, pumpkin seeds, figs, red meat, brown rice and almonds can boost your sex drive – and you can burn off 700 calories an hour while you're at it (so to speak).

Blackcurrants contain more antioxidants than blueberries – and they don't have to travel 6,000 miles to get here. Eat them fresh with cereal or mash and store in the fridge or freezer for use as a fruit sauce for puddings, mixed into low-fat live yoghurt or as the basis for a cold drink.

Broccoli has staggering amounts of vitamin C, vitamin K for bone strength and antioxidants a-go-go making it, frankly, a super-duper-food. Eat it both raw and cooked al dente for maximum impact.

Iron is a crucial mineral for women. Certain breakfast cereals, like All-Bran and Sultana Bran, are fortified with iron; other good sources are sesame seeds and dried apricots.

Kiwifruits have twice the vitamin C of an orange and are also full of vitamin E (good for your skin and for easing arthritis).

Nuts are high in fat but it is 'good fat' because it is monounsaturated and actually protects against heart disease. With high levels of protein, vitamin E and nutrients like zinc and selenium in Brazil nuts, and calcium in almonds and pistachios, they are a 'naughty' snack that will actually do you some good. Double Olympic gold-winner Dame Kelly Holmes confided after the Athens games that 'cashew nuts are my little secret'.

Pomegranate juice Just one 250ml glass of pomegranate juice provides half the recommended daily allowance of vitamins A, C and E – and more antioxidants than red wine, green tea, cranberry or orange juice. Pomegranates are also quoted in the *Kama Sutra* as being the ultimate aphrodisiac.

Seeds offer both protein and minerals. Sunflower seeds are rich in vitamin E; pumpkin seeds are packed with iron.

Tryptophan is an amino acid that is an essential serotonin building block, so for feel-good healthy eating go for sweet peppers, mushrooms, celery, onions, turkey, kelp, parsley, tapioca, watermelon, pecans, mangos, oranges, strawberries, plums, grapefruit, cherries, pineapple, dried dates and papaya.

Zinc is found in foods such as liver, red meat, brazil nuts, wholegrain bread and almonds.

WEIGHTY WORDS

Food is an important part of a balanced diet.

Fran Lebowitz

FAT MEMORY: THE TRUTH BEHIND YO-YO DIETING?

It's blame the old folks time again. Recent research has shown that, while we spend our entire lives struggling to reach our ideal weight – the thinnest we've ever been or what we used to weigh as teenagers – our body has a different goal. It is programmed to store fat to get us back to the highest weight we have ever been. This 'fat memory' dates back to how our body used to survive famines.

Our ancestors needed to eat until they reached a safe weight: fat enough to go for long spells without food. But these days, with abundant food and yo-yo dieting, our fat 'thermostat' gets set artificially high, so the body stores fat unnecessarily, making it very hard to shift.

Tests done on rats and mice – coupled with new understanding of ghrelin and PYY (the sinister-sounding hormones responsible for hunger pangs) and leptin (hormone which controls long-term weight levels) led to the discovery of the 'fat memory'. Finally, there was an explanation for why yo-yo dieters find it so impossible to stay slim – especially after pregnancy and childbirth, when the fat thermostat goes even higher. It's a cruel trick on innocent dieters and no mistaking; a little akin to the peer-pressured decision to shave your legs when you're a teenager, then spending the rest of your life wishing you hadn't because you've just trained your leg hairs to grow back black and bristly…

FIVE STEPS TO TRICKING YOUR 'FAT MEMORY'

1. Exercise: increases your metabolic rate and burns up calories. The extra weight of muscle-building will trick your body into believing you have enough fat stores already – but only if you do about three hours a week and keep it up for life.

2. Long-term loss: Forget following 1,000 calories a day and rapid weight-loss diet plans; concentrate instead on achieving a balanced diet and aim to cut down your food intake by just 100-200 calories a day. This way you don't 'frighten' your fat memory into thinking it's famine time – after two to three days on restricted levels of food, as happens on most diets, your body goes on red alert, releasing hormones which slow down the metabolism. Then, when you go back to eating normally, your metabolism stays at this lower rate, burning fewer calories (even during exercise) as the body is still battling to prevent starvation – and making you even fatter.

3. Avoid binges: As well as a fat memory we have a cognitive memory, making it difficult to adjust to changes in eating patterns. It's that hurling-caution-to-the-wind thing: if you have a pig-out – at Christmas, say, or on a birthday – the temptation is to feel you've blown it so why bother being good again? Not only that but your body will now crave all that food. If you do fall by the wayside, then just try gradually to cut back again over the following few days, rather than abandoning ship and guzzling for an entire week.

4. Eat regularly: Yes, it's the well-tried and exhaustively tested, 'eat little and often' theory. Otherwise the body may think it's threatened with starvation and will send hormones to the stomach that create hunger pangs – then other hormones to make you salivate and increase your awareness of food, making high-fat foods look and smell better than usual.

5. Be patient: This is the toughie: 'It's difficult to put a precise figure on it, but once you gain excess weight, it could take 20 years to reset your body's fat thermostat back to its lower level,' says Tim Spector, professor of genetic epidemiology at St Thomas's Hospital, London. 'So any changes you make really must be for life.' Sigh.

38cm 39cm 40cm 41cm 42cm 43cm 44cm 45cm 46cm 47cm

WILL YOU BE FAT AT 50?

1. Are you or have you ever been overweight? Yes/No
2. Do you rarely eat at least five portions of fruit/veg per day? Yes/No
3. Do you ever skip meals? Yes/No
4. Do you snack between meals? Yes/No
5. Do you ever binge on chocolate or sweets? Yes/No
6. Do you drink more than 14 units of alcohol per week? Yes/No
7. Do you exercise less than three times a week? Yes/No
8. Do you have a sedentary job? Yes/No
9. Do you drive everywhere when you could walk? Yes/No
10. Do you have a family history of weight problems? Yes/No

Ticked Yes 0-3 times: You are unlikely to be fat at 50 but don't get complacent about it.

Ticked Yes 4-7 times: You could be fat at 50 unless you start eating sensibly and/or doing more exercise.

Ticked Yes 8-10 times: Alert! Alert! You are in grave danger of being fat at 50 so take steps to radically change your eating habits and exercise for 30 minutes a day, five times a week.

LETTUCE GIVE THANKS

Lettuce, the humble leaf so painfully associated with the bad old days of dieting, has had a bad press in recent decades. In fact, it's been a symbol of health and fertility since 4,500BC, the era of the Middle Kingdom of Ancient Egypt – as seen in the detailed relief of three cos-style lettuces in the background to Min, the god of fertility, among the carvings at Karnak.

Hippocrates advocated eating it in his diet book, *Regimen*, and the Romans ate it at the end of a meal to induce a mild doziness. Emperor Domitian would serve it before feasts hoping to torture fellow diners by forcing them to stay awake in his presence. This narcotic property was largely forgotten by later lettuce fans until Beatrix Potter had her Flopsy Bunnies falling asleep and nearly being grabbed for Farmer McGregor's pot after eating a surfeit of 'shot' lettuces. While we now live in a golden age of lettuce, from the springiness of lamb's lettuce to the crunch of cos, it wasn't always eaten as salad. Roman cook Apicius recommended lettuce puree with onions, and the *Larousse Gastronomique* declares that lettuce was eaten as a hot dish until the mid-eighteenth century.

38cm 39cm 40cm 41cm 42cm 43cm 44cm 45cm 46cm 47cm

FIVE THINGS YOU NEVER KNEW ABOUT LETTUCE

1. The first Caesar salad was tossed in 1924 by Italian immigrant Caesar Cardini, in Tijuana, Mexico.

2. The word 'lettuce' derives from its Latin name, *lactuca*, which refers to the vegetable's milky latex when cut, which, from one species, is dried like opium and used as a raw material in drug manufacture.

3. Lettuce is the second most popular vegetable in the US, after potatoes. The average American eats about 30lb of lettuce a year.

4. Iceberg lettuce is a crisphead variety and is so-called because it was shipped covered with mounds of ice during the 1920s.

5. Outside the dieting world, there are even lettuce jokes. One example: A man goes to the doctor and says, 'Doctor! Doctor! There's a piece of lettuce sticking out of my nose.' 'Don't worry, my good man, I'll just apply a dressing.'

MORE THINGS THAN YOU EVER THOUGHT POSSIBLE YOU DIDN'T KNOW ABOUT THE ATKINS DIET, A STORY OF FEAST TO FAMINE

■ *Dr Atkins' Diet Revolution* was published in 1972 and immediately attracted criticism from dietitians for its call to slimmers to obtain up to two thirds of their calories from fats and proteins (the famous Atkins bacon-and-eggs breakfast) since the trend then was to tell people to eat less meat, less fat and more pasta. Atkins' response? 'My English sheepdog will figure out nutrition before dietitians do.'

■ Atkins' perseverance paid off with the huge success of the *New Diet Revolution*, revised and re-released in 1992. By the end of the decade, 15 million copies had been sold. In 2004, there were three million followers of Atkins in the UK – and an amazing 32 million in the US.

■ In 2003, there were 442 new product introductions that made a low-carb claim in North America. In 2004, there were 2,602. In August 2005, there were fewer than 700.

■ At its peak, Dr Atkins's *Diet Revolution* was Britain's bestselling tome after *Harry Potter* – more than 120,000 a month in 2003. Only two years later, the Advertising Standards Authority called for an advert for the Atkins Diet to be pulled because its claim that partakers could 'enjoy a healthier lifestyle' could not be substantiated. In July 2005, the company went bust, with debts of £170m.

■ Research company Mintel revealed a high drop-out rate with Atkins. Out of 10% of those questioned who said they had followed one of the low-carb diets and given up, only 1% was willing to try again.

■ Some critics say that the reason Atkins dieters lost weight was not due to 'magic' metabolic change in their body but because they ate fewer calories – partly due to the fact that they filled up quicker on high-protein food and also that the monotony of the food they ate and the complexity of the rules they had to follow meant some people found eating too much bother. About one in seven people quizzed in an AC Nielsen poll said the Atkins plan was just 'too boring'.

■ Dr Atkins's key claim to the success of his diet was that, if a diet was high in protein and fat, the body would start to consume its own fat in a process known as ketosis. But detractors claimed that the side effects of this could include, at best, bad breath and constipation and, at the other end of the spectrum, kidney problems and heart disease.

■ The success of the Atkins regime had one wide-ranging effect: demonising the humble spud. In July 2004, a survey revealed that teenagers in particular had absorbed only one message from the Atkins phenomenon: don't eat potatoes (crisps and chips didn't, apparently, always count because a surprisingly large number of teenagers didn't make the connection between their favourite snacks and, er, the potato). As a result, youngsters were becoming deficient in the minerals contained in vegetables like the plain potato: one in three females aged 11-18 were failing to get enough potassium; two out of five boys and girls aged 11-14 did not eat enough zinc; and more than half of girls aged 11-18 failed to consume the minimum daily magnesium intake.

■ Following the many other health alerts over the diet (increased risk of diabetes, brittle bone disease, depression and breast cancer just to name a few), scientists also warned it could limit a woman's chances of having a healthy baby.

WEIGHTY WORDS

My grandmother started walking five miles a day when she was 60. She's 97 today and we don't know where the hell she is.

Ellen Degeneres

FRAUDS OF THE FOODS

Cereal bars and muesli: A cereal bar rarely has fewer calories than a chocolate bar: a Chocolate Chip Tracker has more calories than a Cadbury's Flake. In a recent study of 86 kinds of cereal, snack and diet bars, only five qualified as 'healthy' – only wholegrains, at least 2g fibre, no more than 1g saturated fat and 14g sugar – and even then the sugar count is high. Muesli is often stuffed with sugar – again, check the label and go for the one with the lowest sugar count.

Fruit: Avoid supermarket fruit salads like the plague: high calorie syrups stop the fruit turning brown – and stop you losing weight. Don't fall for the OJ with breakfast trick: orange juice is high in natural sugars and starts off the day with a sugar spike that'll leave you with sugar cravings all day. Try juicing a mix of veggies and fruits, or drinking V8, which is low in calories and sugar. Another top tip: eat fruit on an empty stomach; fruit eaten after a meal ferments in the gut and can slow down digestion.

Reduced-fat and low-fat foods: According to the Food Standards Agency (FSA), only food that contains less than 3% fat (or less than 3g per 100g) can officially call itself 'low fat', hence the plethora of 'reduced-fat' foods that are nowhere near that low-fat. Even foods labelled as 'low-fat' usually have the same amount of calories as the full-fat option, just derived from a different source: low-fat desserts have more added sugar than regular versions. Don't slather low-fat cream cheese onto Ryvita and pride yourself you're doing well: the fat is only reduced from the extremely high fat count in the regular version. Always check the labels to see how much fat the 'low-fat' product has, bearing in mind that you should only have about 28g fat per day.

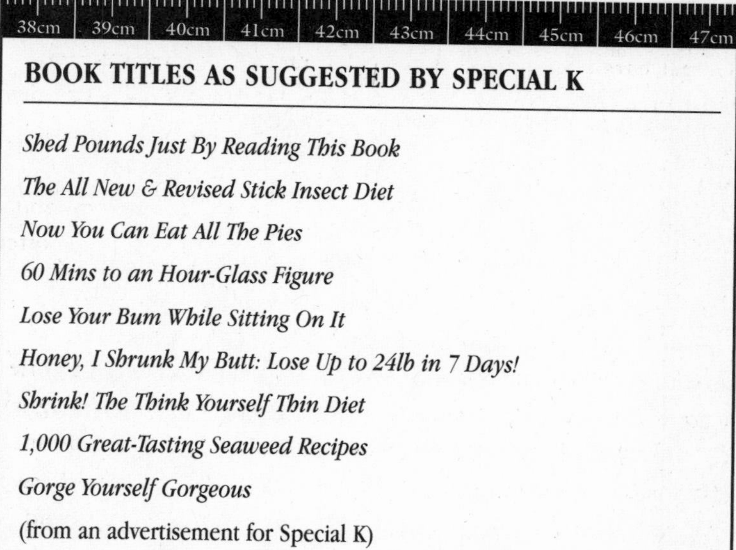

BOOK TITLES AS SUGGESTED BY SPECIAL K

Shed Pounds Just By Reading This Book

The All New & Revised Stick Insect Diet

Now You Can Eat All The Pies

60 Mins to an Hour-Glass Figure

Lose Your Bum While Sitting On It

Honey, I Shrunk My Butt: Lose Up to 24lb in 7 Days!

Shrink! The Think Yourself Thin Diet

1,000 Great-Tasting Seaweed Recipes

Gorge Yourself Gorgeous

(from an advertisement for Special K)

Salads: These are full of hidden dangers and often drowned in fat-soaked dressings. A typical Caesar salad with croutons, cheese and creamy dressing gives you 500 calories and 40g fat per 100g, which makes spaghetti bolognese the less-fattening option. In a restaurant, order the dressing on the side and skip the croutons and bacon bits; at home, try cutting down on dressing by dipping your fork in it rather than pouring it on the salad, then tossing with said fork.

White meat versus red meat versus vegetarianism: Red meat is often shunned as unhealthy but lean beef contains less than 5% fat and is also rich in nutrients like iron. Although chicken is naturally lower in fat and calories it is more often served with rich sauces; and vegetarian foods often rely on cheese and other fatty options for taste, making it extremely calorific.

YET ANOTHER WAY TO EXCUSE YOUR WEIGHT?

The basic premise with this new 'metabolic typing' theory is that there's no such thing as one successful diet for everyone – some foods are good or bad for an individual's health and fitness accordingly. Says Brian Hooper, a former Olympic pole-vaulter and Metabolic Typing advocate, MT is 'like being given a handbook for your body, in the same way you might have one for your car. Just as the car handbook will tell you what oil or petrol to use and which pressure to have the tyres, so MT will tell you which foods and regimes work best in your body.' Testing involves a lengthy questionnaire, after which your 'type' is then subdivided according to your oxidation rate, dominant gland and autonomic nervous system, so after a session with the metabolic mechanics, which metabolic car model might you be?

Protein types metabolise carbohydrates too fast. To balance their body chemistry, they should eat relatively high amounts of proteins and fats. If they eat too many starchy foods, like potatoes, bread and rice, their body compensates by breaking down muscle tissue for a protein source instead of breaking into fat stores for energy burning.

Carbohydrate types metabolise food slowly and need to avoid high-fat proteins. If they eat too much meat, fish, oils or dairy produce their body breaks down muscle tissue for energy, due to a shortage of glucose. They should keep protein levels down to 25% of their daily intake.

Mixed types, needless to say, are more complicated and take a bit of work to calculate where they are on the sliding metabolic scale. They tend not to do well on a restricted diet and need a wide range of foods. Carbs need to be a mix of starchy and non-starchy vegetables, plus simple carb cereals, pasta and wholegrain bread.

'Oh no, it's the lardy of the lake.'

SWEET DRINKS ARE MADE OF THIS

We knew it all along, but diet drinks really are bad for you. A laboratory study done at Purdue University in the US suggests that artificial sweeteners may disrupt the body's natural mechanism for gauging the calorific value of foods. This tricks the body into thinking that all sugary things have no calories so it doesn't factor them into your basic metabolic rate, leading to exponential weight gain the minute you eat anything with sugar, even if it's natural sugar, like that in fruit.

38cm 39cm 40cm 41cm 42cm 43cm 44cm 45cm 46cm 47cm

DO WE BELIEVE THEM? SUPERMODELS' WEIGHT-LOSS 'TIPS'

- Helena Christiensen: 'Moderation is the key. Eat enough of your favourite foods to enjoy the delicious taste but don't overdo it.'
- Linda Evangelista: 'I don't diet. I just don't eat as much as I'd like to.'
- Jerry Hall: 'I eat three balanced meals every day – if you skip meals, your body stores fat. I don't snack and do my best to avoid too much alcohol.'
- Jodie Kidd. 'I went on the Atkins Diet. It was horrendous – I just love chocolate too much. I lasted three days.'
- Elle Macpherson: 'My philosophy is to try to eat food that makes me strong and happy. I believe a healthy body will let you know what food it needs.'
- Claudia Schiffer: 'I don't diet because it messes up your metabolism. I eat three meals a day and I try not to eat in between. All the food I eat is organic.'

THE MIRROR, MIRROR TEST TO SEE IF YOU EAT RIGHT

Acne: If acne hasn't responded to traditional treatments, it may be a sign of polycystic ovary syndrome (PCOS), especially if combined with excess body hair. PCOS can also sometimes account for otherwise inexplicable weight gain.

Ankles: Swollen ankles and legs may indicate heart or circulation problems: detox may be needed.

Back: A tendency to a hunched back near the neck is an early sign of osteoporosis (brittle bone disease) caused by a chronic calcium deficiency. Three portions of dairy products – a glass of skimmed milk, a matchbox-sized piece of cheese and a low-fat yoghurt – can provide the 700-800mg of calcium needed per day.

Hair: While hair loss is usually attributable to either stress or genetic factors, there is some evidence that balding people have a higher risk of coronary heart disease, so check your fat intake.

Hands: If you pluck the skin on the back of your hand and it doesn't immediately spring back into shape, you're dehydrated and not drinking enough water – especially if you're older: the thirst mechanism diminishes as you age.

Skin: Dry and scaly skin can be a sign that you are low in essential fatty acids (found in fish oils, seed oils and nuts) – and can be a symptom of an underactive thyroid gland, which in turn leads to a sluggish metabolism and potential weight gain.

Tongue: Dr Gillian McKeith says there are several ways of analysing a tongue for nutritional deficiencies – a crack down the middle indicates a weak stomach and poor digestion; teeth marks around the edge suggest a sluggish spleen function, especially if you also suffer gas and bloating; horizontal cracks signal malabsorption of B vitamins and a deficiency of energy and, finally, a thick yellow coating (mmm, sounds tasty) indicates bowel problems and a lack of healthy bacteria in the gut.

38cm | 39cm | 40cm | 41cm | 42cm | 43cm | 44cm | 45cm | 46cm | 47cm

HOW BAD IS SALT?

■ High blood pressure, water retention leading to weight gain (particularly in women), kidney disease and cancer of the stomach are just some of the ailments caused by too much salt in the diet.

■ A recent World Health Organisation report highlights that high blood pressure is responsible for half of all cardiovascular deaths – which means it accounts for about 125,000 UK deaths annually.

■ If all adults halved their intake from the current average of 10-12g per day, the number of UK stroke and heart attack victims would fall dramatically – by an estimated 35,000 a year.

■ Three quarters of the salt we eat is said to come from processed foods, from cereals and soups to bakery items and ready meals. A recent survey of high-street sandwiches found one that contained nearly two thirds of the amount of fat women should consume in one day – and 5.2g of salt, which is nearly 86% of an adult's recommended daily intake.

■ With its Sid the Slug ads, the government has set 6g per day as the national maximum per adult, advising three ways to reduce intake: do not add salt to your food at the table; don't add salt to cooking; avoid processed foods which have added salt – foods that have more than 0.2g sodium per 100g – and try to stick to fresh food where salt is naturally lower.

■ In the wake of scare stories like the woman who poisoned her son to death by feeding him salt, and the child who died from the over-salting caused by eating too many Weetabix, it is as well to remember that the recommended daily salt limit for children aged one to three is 2g.

■ To calculate the salt content of food, multiply the sodium by 2.5. As a rule of thumb, 0.5g of sodium (1.25g salt) per 100g is a LOT. And 0.1g of sodium (0.25g salt) per 100g is a LITTLE.

KNOWING YOUR ACRONYMS: WHAT'S YOUR BMI?

Forget your weight or vital statistics, your body mass index, is the preferred indicator of how healthy your weight is. To find yours, divide your weight in kilograms by your height in metres squared. A BMI of between 20 and 25 is considered healthy; 26-30 is overweight, 31-40 is obese and over 40 severely obese.

MORE ACRONYMS: BMR

Just when you thought you knew what BMI was, along comes BMR, your basal metabolic rate. This is the number of calories your body needs just to maintain its basic functions. If you eat 250 calories per day fewer than your BMR, and exercise enough to burn an additional 250 calories per day, you will lose about a pound per week, no questions asked. To determine your BMR, multiply your current weight in pounds by 10. This is roughly how many calories you burn a day while at rest. Depending on how active you are, you need to multiply that figure further:

- Sedentary job (office work) x 1.3
- Moderately active job (shop worker, homemaker) x 1.4
- Active job (postal delivery worker, traffic warden) x 1.5
- Very active job (builder, fitness trainer, courier) x 1.7

This gives the total amount of energy that you burn during an active day. So to lose weight, you just need to eat fewer calories than this and do some exercise to supplement your daytime existence. So a woman homemaker weighing 140lb (10st), has a BMR of 140 x 10 = 1,400 x 1.4 = 1,960 calories per day. If she eats 1,710 calories per day and walks briskly for 45 minutes every day, she'll lose weight. Ta-daa! Now we feel all clever and mathematically brilliant... I wonder if, with all that effort, our BMR went up?

BLAME THE EVIL FOODS AND THEIR INVENTORS

Chocolate chip cookies: Ruth Wakefield, in 1930, was making chocolate cookies at the Toll House Inn in Massachusetts when she ran out of baking chocolate. So she broke up some semi-sweet chocolate and added the pieces to the cookie dough. But instead of melting, they stayed in little chips. An average chocolate chip cookie = 80 calories.

Crisps: A chef called George Crum, cooking at the Moon Lake Lodge in Saratoga Springs, lost his cool when a customer kept sending his potato chips back because they weren't thin and crispy enough. Crum sliced some potatoes paper-thin, fried them until they were brown, called them 'Saratoga Chips' and basked in the glory for the rest of his life. 100g bag of crisps = 540 calories.

Doughnuts: The story goes that a nineteenth-century sea captain used to give his crew pieces of fried dough to eat, and to keep them from hurtling around the deck while the boat pitched about, he jammed them on to the spokes of the ship's helm. Eventually the cook started making them with holes in. Doughnut = 349 calories.

Eggs benedict: A guest at the Waldorf Hotel in New York called Lemuel Benedict asked for a version of eggs benedict as a hangover cure – and the world's most tempting brunch dish was born. Curse you, Lemuel Benedict! Eggs Benedict = 375 calories.

Hot dogs: Legend has it that hot dogs were born in 1901 in New York during a cold baseball game. An ice-cream vendor cooked up a batch of what were called 'dachshund' sausages, put them in rolls and shouted 'Get them while they're red-hot!' A cartoonist portrayed the canny move, drawing barking sausages inside the rolls but he couldn't spell dachshund, so instead he captioned his cartoon 'hot dog'. Average hot dog = 190 calories.

38cm 39cm 40cm 41cm 42cm 43cm 44cm 45cm 46cm 47cm

GI DIET GURU RICK GALLOP'S 10 MANTRAS

1. A rice cake is a diet death.
2. Avoid cheese and caffeine.
3. Cover half your plate with vegetables, a quarter with not complex carbs and a quarter with protein.
4. Eat raw. If you must cook, make everything al dente, making your stomach do the work.
5. Eat regularly to avoid low blood sugar.
6. Eat the fruit rather than drink its juice.
7. Include protein in all meals.
8. Never puree, never mash.
9. Never use sugar, always a substitute.
10. Pasta is a side dish not a meal.

WEIGHTY WORDS

After *One Flew Over the Cuckoo's Nest*, people think the psychiatric ward is where an evil and sadistic person humiliates depressed people. This is actually a far more accurate description of Weight Watchers.

Jo Brand

You get about as much actual food out of eating artichoke as you would licking 30 postage stamps.

Miss Piggy

WEIGHT WATCHERS:
THE STEADY-AS-SHE-GOES PHENOMENON

■ It was started in 1963, around Jean Nidetch's kitchen table, after she decided she was tired of dieting alone so got six girlfriends together to compare notes. It is now the largest, best-known weight-loss programme in the world.

■ Every week more than 43 million people globally go to WW meetings across 30 countries, presided over by 14,000 'leaders' and 34,000 employees, 98% of whom work part-time on commission. The profit margin at 19% is the only fat thing about WW. In Britain alone there are currently one million people actively going to meetings.

■ In the five years after the 'points' system was introduced, the company estimated that, in North America alone, 8.5 million members had lost a total of 86.6 million pounds.

■ Originally, food obsessions were referred to as 'frankensteins' – Jean's own terms.

■ WW went through a low period from 1978 when sold to Heinz, producing drab ready-made meals, but Heinz were bought out in 1999 leading to a renaissance in the company's fortunes.

■ Now it's cool to do WW – in *Sex and the City*, Miranda (red-haired single mother played by Cynthia Nixon) is stopped from buying a diet book by the cashier in a bookstore. 'Weight Watchers,' the cashier tells her, 'is the only sane way to go.' In the next scene Miranda signs up.

■ WW now offers a customised online diet club: you enter your height and weight on the website and it tells you how many daily points you're allowed. Each day you put in what you've eaten and it works out the points you've consumed.

- After two years of research by WW, new programme, 'Switch', is their revamped weight-loss philosophy. Instead of calorie counting, it looks at your lifestyle, behaviour and thought processes so that a diet can be tailored to your needs, and includes the '10 Winning Habits' vital for losing weight for good.

- So far, around 95% of WW clients are women – men are just not interested in the group nature of the programme.

- Sarah Ferguson, the Duchess of York, is now more famous in America for her support of WW (for which she gets paid heftily, over £1m) than for her royal connections. But her contract excludes promoting it in the UK, both for fear of embarrassing those connections and because WW UK severed all ties with her after revelations that she was teaching daughters Beatrice and Eugenie, then aged 12 and 10, to count calories and play diet games.

- A recent WW study tracked 1,000 people who had lost an impressive amount of weight on the WW programme – and found that 80% had kept it off a year later. Even after five years, nearly 50% had avoided putting the weight back on; making WW exponentially more successful than other weight-loss methods. Now GPs are allowed to refer overweight patients to the slimming group and it's even hoped that a widespread partnership will soon be set up with the NHS.

45in 46in 47in 48in

TASTE TEST

It takes eight to 10 attempts to acquire a new taste: so if aduki beans and quinoa a la Gillian McKeith don't sound immediately tempting – try, try, try, try, try, try, try, try, try, try again. It's just a shame it doesn't work the other way – imagine if, when we didn't eat chocolate and oven chips eight to 10 times, we'd lose the taste for them. Oh, nature just isn't playing fair.

BAD FAT, GOOD FAT

Fat has become the watchword for unhealthy living – or, to be precise, unsaturated fat (derived from vegetables) is better for us than saturated fat (which comes mainly from animals). The problem is that most unsaturated fats – let's call them the good fats – are liquid at room temperature, which creates a problem for food manufacturers wanting to include them in their foods. But bubble hydrogen gas through vegetable oil and – via a chemical process involving hydrogen atoms cosying up with long-chain carbon molecules – the oil becomes a solid, and the fats become hydrogenated – leading to spreadable 'butter' replacements, unsoggy quiches and a happy day at the bakery counter. The good news is that hydrogenated fats also prolong the oil's shelf life: how else would those supermarket cakes and biscuits be able to survive for months and months on the shelf?

The bad news is that not only does hydrogenation turn some of the unsaturated 'good' fat into the less healthy, saturated 'bad' fat but it also produces a set of synthetic 'trans' fats. Now, it turns out, trans fats are the real villains of the fatty underworld, putting animal fats well into second place to become Public Fat Enemy Number One. Not only do they raise cholesterol, there's a double whammy involved. At the same time that trans fats decrease the level of HDL cholesterol (the good type of cholesterol – so now you know), they simultaneously raise the LDL cholesterol (the bad, heart-attack-inducing type). Research in the 1990s showed that replacing just 2% of a person's energy intake from trans fats with unsaturated or unhydrogenated fats could slash their chances of getting heart disease by 50%. Separate research has indicated that because trans fats are not naturally occurring our metabolism simply doesn't know what to do with them and just stores them willy-nilly… leading to disproportionate fat cell storage: and cellulite.

Now the Foods Standards Agency (FSA) recommends that trans fats should make up no more than 2% of a person's energy intake. But how do we know? At the moment, trans fats are not labelled in the UK, though food manufacturers were relatively quick in lowering their use of trans fats, bringing the average intake down to a 'safe' average level by 2001. But processed foods like cakes, fat spreads, biscuits, pastries and deep-fried foods can still ramp up your trans fat intake. With even the World Health Organisation weighing in, calling for restrictions on the consumption of trans fats as part of their wider policy on nutrition, it's just yet another reason to cut back on those profiteroles, dammit.

BETTER A BIGGER BUM THAN A BIGGER TUM

If the ratio of a woman's waist to her hip (ie waist divided by hip) is greater than 0.8in, then it is likely that she suffers from high 'visceral' fat – the fat that surrounds the internal organs. This is especially true if her waist measures more than 35in. Visceral fat is associated with higher risk of conditions like heart disease and diabetes.

WEIGHTY WORDS

I never worry about diets. The only carrots that interest me are the number you get in a diamond.

Mae West

Chillies improve metabolism,
So Tracy thought she'd sussed it.
She ate a dozen platefuls,
But spontaneously combusted.

Limerick in a Sveltesse Optimise advertisement.

38cm 39cm 40cm 41cm 42cm 43cm 44cm 45cm 46cm 47cm

GETTING FRUITY: WHICH BODY SHAPE ARE YOU AND WHAT DOES IT MEAN?

■ Apple: Fat is stored around the waist, which raises the risk of diabetes and heart disease. Fat cells padding the tum are more active in producing chemicals, some of which seem to produce an imbalance of proteins and hormones that can damage the body's insulin system. Women with 35in+ waists and men with 40in+ could be at four times the risk of both illnesses.

■ Carrot: Broad on the top half, smaller on the bottom half, with slim waists and hips is the ideal shape, especially for men, but both sexes tend to lay down more fat in later life so beware of maturing into elderly apples.

■ Pear: Small top half and waist, larger bottom, hips and thighs. This is the traditional female shape primed to need fat that is slow-burning to give energy for pregnancy and breastfeeding. However, more and more women are turning apple-shaped, storing their fat mainly around the waist. The pear is healthier than the apple because the fat cells on the thighs and hips tend to be quite inactive, not producing any nasty chemicals to interfere with the body's systems. But these fat cells are notoriously difficult to shift; stomach fat, because it is busy and active, is easier to reduce and is laid down and used up three times as fast.

■ Squash: Short, with short stocky limbs puts you at higher risk of cardiovascular illness and strokes than for tall people – the precursors of which can be poor lung function, high cholesterol levels and more insulin resistance.

■ String bean: tall and thin, with little or no waist. You're less at risk of coronary heart disease but more at risk of cancer – specifically breast cancer, colorectal cancer, leukaemia and lymphomas; possibly because there is a stage during puberty when, for example, developing breast tissue is extremely sensitive to growth hormones, perhaps sowing the seeds for a breast tumour later.

CAN'T GIVE UP THE LATTES?

There's no getting away from the fact that they're fattening, but if lattes and coffees are your real weak point and you want to justify continuing to enjoy the occasional lapse, new research is sticking up for coffee's healthy side, quoting its ability to ward off the following diseases:

Colon cancer: Independent research has shown that drinking at least two cups of coffee a day can reduce the risk of colon cancer by 25%. It also halves the risk of gallstones and helps protect against liver cirrhosis.

Dental cavities: Italian researchers say the compound that gives coffee its bitter taste is both antibacterial and anti-adhesive, so dental plaque and cavities should be reduced.

Diabetes: Coffee, they say, is chockful with antioxidants – which boost the immune system – and magnesium, proven to improve insulin sensitivity and glucose metabolism. Researchers at the Harvard School of Public Health found that six cups a day cut men's risk of type 2 diabetes by 54% and women's by 30%. We're not sure if that includes the hot milk, the cocoa sprinkles and the side order of muffin, however…

Parkinson's disease: At least six studies show regular coffee drinkers are up to 80% less likely to develop Parkinson's. Now caffeine-based drugs for the condition are being developed.

HEALTHY CHOCOLATE... MMM...

First it was red wine, now it's chocolate that has been reprieved from the evil foods guillotine. Research has found that eating dark chocolate can reduce your risk of heart disease, cancer and even diabetes. Hats off to the polyphenols and antioxidants that make a 50g piece of chocolate as 'health-giving' as two glasses of red wine!

PUTTING THE GI DIET THROUGH ITS PACES

The glycaemic index (GI) is rated out of 100, based on the comparative speed at which a food releases sugar into the bloodstream. When your body detects sugar in the blood it triggers the pancreas to release insulin, a hormone that removes excess glucose from the blood to return levels to normal. If insulin levels are high because of high blood sugar, the excess glucose will be stored as fat; the GI diet keeps insulin levels low (and therefore no excess glucose to be stored as fat) which encourages your body to burn fat instead.

High-GI foods give a sugar high but the subsequent low makes reaching for something else to eat an inevitability – so sugar levels peak and trough precariously throughout the day. Low-GI foods provide a slow and steady supply of energy. Any food with a GI rating of 55 and under has been given the OK by GI gurus; wholemeal bread has a rating of 53, porridge made with water is a healthy 44. Dieters stay satisfied for longer and are less likely to snack; weight loss isn't dramatic but equally slow and steady and achieved in a relatively pain-free way – always combined with common sense calorie-counting. White rice, for example, is evil incarnate, with a GI of 98, giving an almost instant sugar hit – then crash.

Though developed into diets by Australian Professor Jennie Brand-Miller and Canadian Rick Gallop, the GI was actually created in 1981 by a nutrition professor at the University of Toronto, Dr Jenkins, and used to help people with diabetes to regulate their blood sugar levels. Unlike Atkins' *New Diet Revolution*, however, there are no rights to the GI concept, which probably initially stalled its progress – hence why every man and his dog (Antony Worrall-Thompson, Gillian McKeith, Joanna Hall) is now able to publish their own version of the GI diet.

An animal study published in *The Lancet* in August 2004 found that a low-GI diet can lead to weight loss, as well as reducing the risk of developing diabetes and cardiovascular disease, giving the diet an objective kudos that Atkins never quite managed.

'It's the advice we've been giving for the past 10 years,' says Claire MacEvilly (and no, she's not an evil scientist from *The X Men* but a nutritionist at the MRC Human Nutrition Research Laboratory in Cambridge), 'but with these added labels of high and low GI.' There's nothing like a new lingo to keep the dieting classes happy.

It isn't all just common sense, however – certain discrepancies present themselves which seem counter-intuitive to losing weight. Crisps, which contain a lot of fat, have a low GI rating because fat slows down the absorption rate of the potato – so a baked potato, on the other hand, is a no-no. A raw carrot has a relatively low GI but, once cooked, making it more readily digested, it has a high value – incredibly, higher than chocolate.

The traffic light system, as adopted by Tesco for 1,000 of its products, does take into account the food's calorific and fat content as well as its GI rating: red are the foods we should avoid; amber can be eaten in moderation and green, er, gives you the green light to eat away.

The future may well see the development of foods bioengineered to modulate blood sugar levels, transforming traditionally high-GI foods into low-GI, healthier options. Tesco is currently sponsoring research and development into an understanding of what lowers the GI of a given food: the 'Holy Grail' of a GI-filled future.

It is claimed that this way of eating can help increase serotonin production – so eating the GI way can even make you happy – and not many diets can promise that.

38cm 39cm 40cm 41cm 42cm 43cm 44cm 45cm 46cm 47cm

TOP 10 REASONS WHY DIETS ARE BETTER THAN SEX

1. You don't have to take off your clothes
2. You can go from diet to diet without feeling guilty
3. Celery is *always* hard
4. On a diet you carefully consider everything you put in your mouth
5. It's *good* if a diet is over quickly
6. Dieting doesn't make you pregnant
7. You can doze off in the middle of a diet if you want to
8. It's OK if your dog watches you diet
9. You can do it with your best friend's husband
10. You don't have to worry if it was good for the cottage cheese, too

TELL 'EM ABOUT THE HONEY, MUMMY

Could this be the ultimate diet for couch potatoes? You eat honey just before going to bed, instead of spending hours at the gym, thereby allowing the honey to cause our metabolism to burn our fat as we sleep. Mike McInnes, a leading Scottish nutritionist and the discoverer of the 'hibernation diet', came up with the idea after working with Scottish athletes. The first four hours of sleeping, when we go into slow-wave sleep, is the most important time for fat-burning since it is when we turn on the pituitary gland and the hormones that break down and use fat as a fuel. By eating honey, the liver is fuelled and free to work on burning fat, rather than stabilising blood glucose levels. Sounds great but is anyone else grappling with an image of those old *Beezer* comic characters, the Numskulls?

WEIGHTY WORDS

The worst thing that ever happened to me was that I offered a fellow a crisp from my bag – and he took two.

Vic Reeves

Backstage at the Fashion Awards, the models were so nervous they were keeping their food down.

Jack Dee

Self-delusion is pulling in your stomach when you step on the scales.

Paul Sweeney

38cm 39cm 40cm 41cm 42cm 43cm 44cm 45cm 46cm 47cm

YOU ARE WHAT YOU BONK: DR GILLIAN MCKEITH'S DIET GUIDE TO A BETTER SEX LIFE

- Strawberries and other berries, she says, pep up your sex drive, because of all the antioxidants they contain. Her 'Ultra Sexy Starter' smoothie contains two handfuls of raspberries, two handfuls strawberries, one peach and one banana, all whizzed up and poured over half a cup of blueberries for the perfect breakfast in bed.
- Artichokes heat up your genitalia so steam some for a steamy evening.
- Oats energise your thyroid, so eat a bowl of porridge in the morning if you want to get your oats at night.
- Avocados, tomatoes, beetroot and sauerkraut are all good for feeding the brain and the nervous system leading down to the sex organs.

NOT JUST THE STORY OF THE FISHES AND THE LOAVES

Diets inspired by the Bible are the new big thing in America. 'What Would Jesus Eat?' is no longer a rhetorical question but one of the latest bestselling diet books, along with the Hallelujah Diet, the Creationist Diet, the Lord's Table, the Prayer Diet, the Maker's Diet and the Weigh Down Diet, where disciples can eat anything they want but must use the power of their faith to grant them divine moderation in all things (a clearly revolutionary concept not familiar to any woman who has ever passed a bakery and prayed, 'Oh Lord, please don't let them have put the fresh doughnuts in the window today!').

Presumably going on the premise that in 2,000 years of iconography, no one has ever seen a fat picture of Jesus – and not wanting in any way to cash in on America's annual £22bn slimming industry (despite the indications – books, DVDs, courses – to the contrary), the diets are variation on a similar theme. Most look to the Bible for justification: like Genesis 1:29, 'And God said, "Behold, I have given you every herb bearing seed which is upon the face of all the earth, and every tree, in which is the fruit of a tree yielding seed; to you it shall be for meat".'

The idea is to be mostly vegetarian (though the Hallelujah Dieters eschew all animal products except for honey) and following a basically Mediterranean diet that has remained unchanged through the millennia: fresh unprocessed food, modest helpings of fish and meat, lightly cooked vegetables, olive oil and fruit, washed down with a little wine and bread. Cynics say there is no science or dieting logic here; supporters tuck into their dinners and say: 'God designed our body and he gave us the signals to obey. If we overstuff ourselves, we are disobeying.' Southern Baptists, meanwhile, are up in arms at the idea that pious dieters should even contemplate alcohol, when they preach abstinence across the board.

WEIGHTY WORDS

I'm a binge eater, chocoholic, sit at my desk day and night, can't be bothered to weigh foods or count calories, but help: I am vain! Rick Gallop's chart will be taped to my forearm in restaurants – and on the fridge. This is my diet book for ever.

Barbara Amiel, pundit, columnist and wife of beleaguered media baron Conrad Black

At a Weight Watchers meeting, one woman was heard to say to another – 'What finally decided me was overhearing my son threatening our neighbour's son with: "My mummy's bigger than your mummy!"'

Punch magazine

Fitness – if it came in a bottle, everybody would have a great body.

Cher

Two cannibals eating a clown. One says to the other, 'Does this taste funny to you?'

Tommy Cooper

If nature had intended our skeletons to be visible it would have put them on the outside of our bodies.

Elmer Rice

Well, go ahead, and eat, and grow fat. Become ugly, heavy, have asthma attacks and die, choked by your own fat

Tell us what you really think, M Brillat-Savarin, celebrated French gourmet

hmm..maybe in 2012!
FRIDGIDAIRE
CALENDAR
SHE REALISED IT WOULD BE FOOLISH TO START A DIET WITH THIRD COUSIN RODNEY'S RETIREMENT PARTY DUE IN ONLY 12 YEARS

THE SENSIBLE CHAPTER

Only a diet that helps you change your way of eating permanently is any good. It shouldn't have to be about having to stick to strange food for life but about shifting patterns to lose the weight, then keep it off. In my view, it's all about coming back to basics: fresh, wholesome, unprocessed food with a minimal amount of the things we just know aren't good for us – fried foods, sugar and manufactured junk

Natalie Savona, dietitian

This concluding chapter is rather like the back of a crossword or sudoku book: it's the one with the answers. We can't deliver a miracle cure for being fat – or an exercise regime that doesn't require effort – but we will attempt to cut through the conflicting advice and offer little bitesized tips for making weight control less daunting.

For every new diet, diet pill or scientific discovery, there is another that contradicts it. This is the awful reality of dieting today. So we make no apologies for sticking with homely homilies and tried-and-tested tips. Some of them are biased – we tend to disagree with the basic tenets of Atkins and agree with the principles behind the glycaemic index but that's as specific as we'll get. Nor will we pass judgement on whether you're a diet obsessive or a fattie longing for an excuse never to have to diet again: read between the lines and you'll see that this chapter is for both of you. Think of us as your wise old grandmother: you're prepared to give her the benefit of the doubt when it comes to homespun wisdom but you wouldn't expect her to know how to split the atom, would you?

LOSE WEIGHT WITHOUT NOTICING

Here's how:

- Park on the far side of the car park at the supermarket.

- If you're not doing a big shop, use a basket instead of a trolley.

- Do bicep curls with shopping bags on the way back to the car.

- Buy fruit and veg that you have to peel or chop up; they're not only better for you, you'll burn five times as many calories in their preparation than just ripping open a packet.

- Throw away the television remote control.

- Take the stairs not the lift.

- Get off the bus one stop early and walk the rest of the way.

- In the office, don't email your colleagues, walk over and talk to them instead.

- Tone your legs while holding them up straight in front of you under your desk while you type.

- Look upon housework as weight-loss opportunity and play lively music while you clean – it subconsciously encourages you to put in more effort. As you take dishes out of the dishwasher, turn your body from side to side, allowing your hips to turn so that your torso twists while you reach to put them in the cupboard. Put dishes away one at a time. Practise squats as you put things away in low cupboards: stand up straight and slowly bend your knees so that your bum is stuck out behind you, as though you are sitting on an invisible chair. You'll look like a complete moron but who needs Jane Fonda to tone up?

- Wear fewer layers of clothes in winter – using common sense – and turn down the thermostat: you'll have to move more to keep warm and your metabolism will speed up to keep your core temperature up.

- Laugh out loud (a form of internal jogging), fidget, jiggle your knees at your desk – every little bit helps both to burn calories and to keep metabolism raised in the long term.

- Walking around while you're on the phone can burn 80 calories during a 20-minute conversation.

- Chomping sugar-free gum burns around 11 calories per hour – and stops you putting more evil things into your mouth.

- Drink ice-cold water – your body uses up more calories bringing it up to body temperature.

- Express your anger – having a good stomp about does wonders for blood flow, metabolism and might even spur you to storm off round the block; whereas repressing irritation has been shown to increase the risk of heart disease by as much as 75%.

- When you book a holiday, don't just plump for the same old lie-on-the-beach fall-back. Whether it's learning to tango in Argentina, horse-riding in Spain, climbing Kilimanjaro in Tanzania, cycling in France or walking in Italy you can enjoy a new experience, pep up your system and maybe even lose some weight while you're at it.

- Every time you start to eat something, just ask yourself why you're eating. Maybe you're confusing thirst with hunger – so try having a glass of water instead.

WEIGHTY WORDS

I wave the flag of 'don't go on diets because they're rubbish' but I had to get the baby weight off or I wouldn't work. My bottom looked like purple broccoli and my other body parts resembled squashes. How can you feel sexy when you look like the back end of a bus?

Kate Winslet says it for post-natal mums everywhere

I've become the world's greatest fat-ass mother. I don't think it's a tragedy. Tragedies are happening all over the world and I'm not a tragedy.

Kirstie Alley

I don't overeat because I was slapped by my mother when I was five. I overeat because I'm a damned hog.

Dolly Parton

I'm fat and proud of it. If someone asks me how my diet is going, I say, 'Fine, how was your lobotomy?'

Roseanne

Sex is about as important as a cheese sandwich. But a cheese sandwich, if you ain't got one to put in your belly, is extremely important.

Ian Dury

Fat people are brilliant in bed. If I'm sitting on top of you, are you going to argue?

Jo Brand

RESTAURANT SWAPS

Eating out doesn't have to spell diet disaster – even in those high-fat havens, the Chinese, the Indian and the Italian, there are options that are less evil than others:

Chinese: One serving of prawn toast is enough to tip the rest of your meal into the red (590 calories). A whole meal of vegetable wonton soup, steamed rice, stirfried prawns with veg and some lychees for pudding has the same value (590 calories).

Indian: Instead of lamb biryani and keema naan (1,130 calories) try tandoori prawns, boiled pilau rice and chickpea and spinach curry (520 calories).

Italian: Prosciutto and spaghetti bolognese, followed by apple tart (1,210 calories)? Why not try tomato soup, pasta primavera, a small green salad and two scoops of sorbet (550 calories).

Restaurant rules of thumb? Order two starters instead of a starter and main course – and make up the difference with a green salad, dressing on the side, or a side plate of steamed vegetables. Try, try, try to hold back from diving into the bread basket; have a large glass of water instead to fill you up momentarily until your ordered food arrives. Don't feel you have to finish everything on your plate – even the grandest of restaurants won't stick their nose in the air if you ask to box up the excess and take it home.

WEIGHTY WORDS

There are only two types of exercise in Hollywood – jogging and helping a divorced friend move.

Robert Wagner

AVOID COMMON DIET TRAPS

Night-time snacking: Clean your teeth straight after dinner so you're not tempted to snack later. And avoid junk food ads on TV.

Drinking without thinking: Since alcohol is a diet disaster, try alternating each drink you want with a big glass of water – and avoid just chucking back the wine without thinking; savour it with small sips.

Convenience foods: Being busy or hunting round for foods to have on your office lunch hour are common bugbears, but everywhere sells fruit for people on the run.

Skipping meals: You know the received wisdom – a meal skipped is a later meal pigged out on.

Cravings: If you get the urge, wait 15 minutes. If you still want it, go ahead but the chances are that the craving will have passed.

Being inflexible: It's important to indulge – give yourself one day off a week if you're being strict and have your favourite food when you really, really want it: you'll actually crave it less when it's no longer forbidden fruit.

Social slip-ups: Research shows you eat 50% more with friends than when you're alone – so talk more, eat less. And don't feel the need to have the same size portions as your partner.

WEIGHTY WORDS

A cucumber should be well-sliced, and dressed with pepper and vinegar, and then thrown out, as good for nothing.

Samuel Johnson

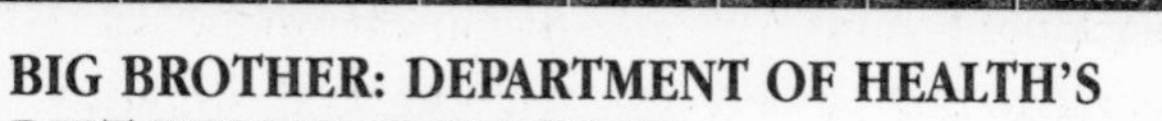

BIG BROTHER: DEPARTMENT OF HEALTH'S DIET RECOMMENDATIONS

Our first reaction on reading these was annoyance at the patronising tone – 'eat the right amount' indeed – but, sigh, they're right. You know they're right.

1. Enjoy your food
2. Eat a variety of different foods
3. Eat the right amount to be a healthy weight
4. Eat plenty of foods rich in starch and fibre
5. Eat plenty of fruit and vegetables
6. Eat fish at least twice a week and make one portion an oily fish like mackerel, sardines, salmon or pilchards.
7. Don't eat too many foods that contain a lot of fat
8. Don't have sugary foods and drinks too often
9. If you drink alcohol, drink sensibly

KEEPING UP WITH THE JONESES' DIARY

Study after study has shown that keeping track of how much you eat and exercise in a food diary is the key to losing weight and keeping it off. A group of dieters that kept detailed food diaries during a 15-week study lost 64% more weight than those who didn't. Another study found that, out of 10 ways to change eating habits, self-monitoring was the only one that allowed people to keep off lost weight.

MAKING SENSE OF THE EXERCISE ROLLERCOASTER

However you choose to interpret the cast-iron maxim that we need to be more active, bear in mind the following tips:

- Exercise increases one's metabolic rate for between six and 36 hours afterwards. Going for a brisk walk before eating your main meal will set you up for an energy-efficient calorie intake.

- For exercise to be effective, we have to work our heart at between 60-85% of its maximum rate (or beats per minute) which is known as the training zone. To work out your heart's maximum rate, take the number 220 and subtract your age from it. So if you're 35, your heartbeat while exercising should be 220 – 35 = 185 x 60% = 111 beats per minute. Test your heartbeat by counting the pulse in your wrist over 15 seconds and multiplying that by four. Clear as mud?

- Exercise – whether it's formal workouts or just being one step beyond active for 20 minutes a day – has to be regular.

- Resistance is a good way to offset the declining metabolic rate typically found as we age: the perfect weekly workout routine for thirtysomethings and above includes both resistance training and aerobic training. Resistance also creates muscle – and muscle automatically burns nine times more calories than fat; you'll burn calories even when you're asleep – and weights don't have to be involved as you can use your own body weight as resistance with moves like lunges, press-ups, squats and crunches.

- The improvement in blood pressure which occurs after exercise has now been shown to increase blood flow, sending the blood racing to your pelvic region and getting you in the mood for love – therefore raising your sex drive.

GI QUICK-FIX TRICKS: LOWER THE GI OF YOUR MEAL

- If you crave the odd baguette, make it a wholemeal pitta bread and fill it with a salad – ideally one that contains beans, like kidney or cannellini beans.
- Add sweetcorn to salads and sandwiches to lower their GI.
- While peanut butter is high in calories, it sometimes works to have it – or something else packed with protein, like nuts – for breakfast because its low GI will stop you craving unhealthy snacks before lunchtime.
- Acids such as vinegar and lemon juice reduce a food's GI rating – so add these as dressings to your food.
- Swap mashed potatoes for al dente new potatoes; easy cook or white rice for basmati, brown or wild rice.
- Instead of chips 'n' dip, try dipping sugar snap peas in tzatziki made from low-fat yoghurt, or home-made hummus (try to stint on the olive oil, with lemon juice).

TOP TIPS FOR DESPAIRING MUMS

Cooking home-made food is just plain better than ripping open a packet, so lose the preconception that it's too time-consuming. And don't despair: it takes between 10-15 attempts on average before children accept a new vegetable; Involving children in the cooking process often predisposes them to like what's being cooked; apply the 'rod for own back' rule whenever you're tempted to give in just to shut them up. If you give them a sweet after tea, it sends them into an irritating sugar high and creates the precedent so you'll have to do the same the next day, and the next and the next…

PLASTIC SURGERY WITHOUT THE COST

• Give yourself a 'council-house facelift' – a high, tight ponytail that makes the face and neck so taut that even posture is improved.

• Give yourself a facelift at your desk: the 'swan' is an exercise that helps tighten sagging skin around the throat, firms the jawline and lifts the breast tissue: breathe in while sitting up straight and relaxed, breathe out through your nose and, while doing so, drop your head slowly forward and gently pull your chin in towards your chest. Hold the position for five seconds. Breathe in carefully while carefully tipping your head backwards – only as far as possible – and sticking out your chin. Keep your mouth closed and lengthen your neck as you breathe out. Feel the stretch under your chin. Hold the position for five seconds. Do this several zillion times and you'll have a chinline as sharp as Reese Witherspoon's.

• Concentrate on cheating the camera. Instead of saying 'cheese', dip your chin down and look up at the camera (think Princess Diana but less squirmingly bashful). As you smile, push your tongue hard into the the roof of your mouth – *et voila*, instant disappearance of double chin.

• Give yourself a tummy tuck – and the illusion of having lost half a stone – by standing up straight and pulling your tummy in. Hard to remember? Draw your belly button inwards, gently pulling in the abdominals and then tie a piece of string around the narrowest part of your waist while holding this position. Then, whenever you slump or let your tummy sag, you'll feel it pressing against the string and be reminded to pull it in.

• Forget expensive 'whitening' treatments for teeth: bleach them naturally by rubbing strawberries over them.

• Rub age spots with vinegar or the inside of banana skins instead of squandering cash on useless expensive creams.

• For a youthful complexion, use the inside of a mango or papaya skin to exfoliate instead of clinical microdermabrasion.

• Get a cheap trout pout by mixing Vaseline with sugar and rubbing it into the lips.

• Forget seaweed wraps: massage cellulite with real coffee grounds while in the shower.

38cm 39cm 40cm 41cm 42cm 43cm 44cm 45cm 46cm 47cm

SNACK ATTACK – NOT PREPARED TO GIVE UP THOSE NIBBLES IN FRONT OF THE TELLY?

■ Try air-popped popcorn with nothing added – and use chopsticks to slow yourself down.

■ Pretzels, made of baked wheat, are practically fat free but do try to chip the rock salt off for an extra healthy halo.

■ For sweet tooths, sesame snaps may still be fattening but they are at least rich in omega-3 oils and the crunchy texture helps ease your appetite faster than chocolate.

■ Avoid roasted or salted nuts: chew carefully on almonds, brazil nuts, hazelnuts or cashews – or have a mixture of pumpkin, sunflower and sesame seeds.

■ If you can face the faff, the best ever snacks are edamame – Japanese soybeans – which are nothing but good for you. Steam the whole pod and pop out the beans from inside – delicious, and the effort and time spent on popping them cuts down calorific intake.

IS IT WORTH BUYING ORGANIC FOOD?

Apples and pears: Yes, pesticides can linger on the peel.

Broccoli, peas and onions: No, these were among the surprising foods that, when non-organic varieties were tested, were showed to have insubstantially low pesticide residues.

Cereals: No, like wheat, rye and oats: in tests only 16% of grains had any detectable pesticide residues, so non-organic is OK.

Fizzy drinks: No, water is neither organic or non-organic and the rest of a fizzy drink is just sugar.

Fruit and veg with non-edible peel: No, any pesticide residue is almost certainly discarded with the peel so go for ordinary (or Fairtrade, if you still want to do your bit for developing nations) avocadoes, bananas, mangoes, pineapples, kiwifruit, papaya, oranges and lemons.

Green leaves: Yes, along with potatoes, organic spinach, lettuce and cabbage were found to have more vitamin C, magnesium, iron and phosphorus than non-organic varieties in trials.

Meat: Yes, non-organic livestock and chickens are fed antibiotics and growth hormones that studies have linked to antibiotic resistance and cancer.

Milk: Yes, organic milk has 50% more vitamin E, 75% more vitamin A and is up to three times richer in antioxidants.

Soup: Yes, organic vegetable soups have been shown to contain six times as much salicylic acid as non-organic broths, which helps fight heart disease and bowel cancer.

Worst offenders: the non-organic foods most contaminated with pesticides are pears, peaches, raspberries, apples, strawberries, spinach, celery, potatoes and peppers, so go organic on these at least.

38cm 39cm 40cm 41cm 42cm 43cm 44cm 45cm 46cm 47cm

AVOID PORTION DISTORTION

You may be eating the right things, but are you eating too much of them? Here's a handy rule of thumb guide:

- Nuts and cheese: golf ball
- Meat and fish: deck of cards
- Oils and fats: dice
- Vegetables: tennis ball
- Starchy carbs (bread, pasta, rice, potatoes): computer mouse or half a tennis ball

38cm 39cm 40cm 41cm 42cm 43cm 44cm 45cm 46cm 47cm

RICK KAUSMAN'S TIPS FROM HIS BOOK: IF NOT DIETING, THEN WHAT?

- Enjoy food without feeling guilty.
- Increase your eating awareness – learn to taste food, eat it slowly, savour it.
- Stop worrying about fat, food, size and shape.
- Improve how you feel about yourself.
- Enjoy being active.
- Achieve and maintain a healthy, comfortable weight for you, without being deprived of food or quality of life.

TOOLS TO WARD OFF TEMPTATION

Move4Health is a pedometer that is both check and motivation. A recent report by the National Register of Weight Loss showed slimmers who lost 60lb (4st 4lb) and kept it off for five years burned off more than 2,800 calories through exercise each week. What's increasingly the case is that they were doing this not just through going to the gym or taking regular exercise classes but just by being more active in their everyday life. A pedometer is the perfect tool to monitor this, aiming for a minimum of 10,000 paces each day.
Costs £19.99 (www.sportex.net)

Nutracheck Mobile is a downloadable programme (you'll need a GPRS phone) that gives you calorie counts on the move – in supermarkets, pubs and even fast food outlets – and a running total of calories consumed. If you're a calorie obsessive, you'll love the thought of being able to check the calorie and fat content of more than 20,000 food and drink items at the press of a button.
Costs £9.99 a month (www.nutracheck.co.uk)

Ketone Home Screening Test is for dieters, whichever regime they are on, to see rock-solid proof that their body is burning fat. OK, so it's less than glamorous peeing on a stick but the test can show how many ketones your body is producing and therefore how much stored fat is being burned – all within less than a minute.
Costs £9.99 for 25 test strips (www.homechec.co.uk)

Masai Barefoot Technology shoes will, it is claimed, improve posture, flexibility and cellulite and help you to burn up to five times as many calories as you would with regular shoes. The jury is out and they look a bit daft but they've been used widely in European orthopaedic clinics for years and genuinely seem to help a wide range of musculo-skeletal problems.
Cost from £135 (www.mbt-uk.com)

The Diet Plate has drawn lines and helpful pictures for different food groups, showing you the 'boundaries' of what you want to eat, in order to stick inside the recommended portion and calorie amount. A study in Ohio has found that controlling your portions is a quicker and easier way to lose weight than upping exercise, eating more fruit and veg or cutting down on fat, and the Diet Plate offers a relatively fuss-free way of achieving that control.
Costs from £17 (www.thedietplate.com)

BodyGem is a handheld gizmo that can measure how fast you burn calories. An easy breath test measures your oxygen consumption, then calculates the rate that your body burns calories at when you're resting, which is about 75% of your day. As you take more exercise, you should see your metabolism speeding up – what better motivation do you need?
Costs £445 or you can be measured for free if you sign up to Virgin Active (0845 1304747) gyms (www.virginactive.co.uk)

38cm 39cm 40cm 41cm 42cm 43cm 44cm 45cm 46cm 47cm

DEM BONES, DEM BONES

With all the concern about osteoporosis and the detrimental effect that dieting is having on our bone density, it's as well to have a calcium checklist that either won't pile on the pounds or will justify the occasional treat of chocolate:

- 100g cheddar: 729mg calcium
- 100g steamed tofu: 510mg calcium
- 100g milk chocolate: 200mg calcium
- 100g watercress: 170mg calcium

To prevent osteoporosis, have 700-800mg calcium every day.

THE 24-HOUR DANGER ZONE

Nutritionist Anita Bean recommends steering clear of the following foods 24 hours before a big night out, to look your best in your party clothes:

Beans: Pulses, beans and lentils are fabulous foods but can leave you feeling gassy and bloated so lay off them just before the party.

Fizzy drinks: Drinking fizzy drinks will puff you up with carbon dioxide and give you an unnecessary spare tyre.

Salty stuff: Read the labels and cut back on salt before a big event as it causes water retention.

Stir-fries: Cauliflower, cabbage and broccoli react with other foods in the gut and cause flatulence so give yourself a break from these super-foods.

Wheat: It's not a hardship if you give up bread and pasta for a day or so – and wheat can make you bloat.

38cm 39cm 40cm 41cm 42cm 43cm 44cm 45cm 46cm 47cm

RULE OF THUMB FOR FEEDING CHILDREN

What each child needs each day:

- Three servings of vegetables
- Two of fruit
- Four to six servings of grains and/or potatoes
- Two servings of calcium-rich foods (such as milk or cheese)
- Two servings of protein-rich foods (such as lean meat or eggs)
- One serving (about a tablespoon) of healthy fats and oils

LIGHT AT THE END OF THE TUNNEL

What, after all, is overweight? A study conducted by the University of Colorado – the comfortingly named 'Obesity Myth' – says that our current set of measurements for obesity and fatness is set too low and that we have allowed ourselves to be distracted and misled by the health dangers of the extremely obese. It also suggests that being a bit underweight could be worse than being a bit plump – and that having larger fat stores is linked to living longer.

Based on the new calculations, excess weight is no longer the second leading cause of death in the US after smoking, but the seventh. 'Large-scale studies have shown that people with a BMI of 26-28 have the highest life expectancy,' says the author Paul Campos, 'while people with a BMI of 18-20 and less (Victoria Beckham 17, Catherine Zeta Jones 19) actually have a lower life expectancy than the officially "obese" with a BMI between 34-36.'

38cm 39cm 40cm 41cm 42cm 43cm 44cm 45cm 46cm 47cm

TEMPTING TONGUE TWISTERS TO TURN TIPPLERS' THOUGHTS AWAY FROM TUCKER

- A box of biscuits, a batch of mixed biscuits
- If Stu chews shoes, should Stu choose the shoes he chews?
- Mrs Smith's Fish Sauce Shop
- Fred fed Ted bread and Ted fed Fred bread
- Friendly Frank flips fine flapjacks
- Selfish shellfish
- If Peter Piper picked a peck of pickled peppers, where's the peck of pickled peppers Peter Piper picked?

AQUAHOLIC

Almost all health professionals are united on one tip for dieters – drinking water, and plenty of it. But do try not to overdose, difficult as that may sound, and bear in mind the cautionary tale of Tina Christopherson. The 29-year-old Florida woman, who had an IQ of 189 so should have known better, became obsessed with the idea that she suffered from stomach cancer, a disease that had killed her mother. In an attempt to cleanse her body, Christopherson went on periodic water fasts, during which she ate no food but drank up to four gallons of water a day. By 17 February 1977, she had consumed so much water that her kidneys were overwhelmed and the excess fluid drained into her lungs. She died of internal drowning, otherwise known as 'water intoxication'.

38cm 39cm 40cm 41cm 42cm 43cm 44cm 45cm 46cm 47cm

EASY SWAPS

1. Swap white rice for brown
2. Swap pasta for soya or chickpea pasta (at the very least, get wholemeal pasta) and regular noodles for buckwheat noodles
3. Swap milk chocolate for dark chocolate if you must have a treat
4. Swap white bread for wholegrain bread
5. Swap wheat cereals for porridge oats
6. Swap vegetable oil for olive oil
7. Swap mayonnaise for home-made olive oil-based dressing
8. Swap fizzy drinks for water or herbal teas: green tea even boosts the metabolism
9. Swap baked potatoes for baked sweet potatoes
10. Swap fruit juices for fresh fruit

DID YOU KNOW?

The less we sleep, the more weight we gain, according to recent research. Sleep deprivation also boosts your appetite and makes it harder to feel motivated about taking exercise.

In an average person's lifetime they eat around 35 tonnes of food.

The average person opens the fridge 22 times a day.

Most people have lost 50% of their taste buds by the time they reach 60 – the average lifespan of each taste bud is 10 days.

WEIGHTY WORDS

I suppose you really do believe that your happiness is consequent on your size? That an inch or two one way or the other would make you truly loved? It would be excusable in a 16-year-old – if my nose were a different shape, if my bosom were larger, then the whole world would be different. But in a woman of your age, it is vulgar.

Fay Weldon, *The Fat Woman's Joke*

Erotic is when you use a feather. Kinky is when you use the whole chicken.

Anon

ORGANIC: THE GRASS ROOTS VIEW

Buying organic food will automatically set you on the right road to weight loss because it will get you thinking about what you're putting in your mouth – but it's expensive. Save your pennies for the organic foods that really matter and go for the value box on the others.

SPUD-U-LIKE

It's not quite a licence to eat crisps and chips but researchers at the Australian Centre of Neuropsychotherapy have found that eating steam-cooked potatoes is one of the easiest ways to ward off Seasonal Affective Disorder (SAD). Don't go adding butter though – or you'll just be sunk in gloom that you still can't get into that little black dress for the office Christmas party.

WEIGHTY WORDS

Diet tip: Never eat anything at one sitting that you can't lift.

Miss Piggy

The way to keep your health is to eat what you don't want, drink what you don't like and do what you'd rather not.

Mark Twain

The name Big Mac is generally supposed to have come about because it is a big McDonald's burger, but in fact it was named after a big raincoat whose taste it so closely resembles.

Jo Brand

38cm 39cm 40cm 41cm 42cm 43cm 44cm 45cm 46cm 47cm

IF YOU ONLY DO ONE THING…

■ If you only do one detox thing – drink lots of water throughout the day.

■ If you only take one vitamin – make it a multivitamin with minerals.

■ If you avoid only one food – make sure it's refined sugar found in junk food, processed food, cakes and biscuits.

■ If you only do one beauty thing – get your sleep by forcing yourself to bed one hour earlier.

■ If you have to have one drink – drink a Seabreeze: vodka has less calories than wine and is purer than most drinks – while cranberry and grapefruit juices are good diuretics and rich in antioxidants.

■ If you have to have one night on fast food – eat thin-crust pizza – with as much tomato as possible, which is rich in the heart-protecting antioxidant lycopene – and blot it with a piece of kitchen roll: eliminating around 14% of the total fat.

■ If you have to have one fried meal – use oil sprays and brushes to make a little oil go a long way. If roasting veg, shake them in a bag with just a couple of teaspoons of olive oil. Sure you can't barbecue or grill whatever you wanted to fry?

■ If you have to have one cake – make it a carrot or banana cake at home where it won't have anything like the same level of fat as shop-bought, long-life versions and is packed with fruit into the bargain

This stuff tastes awful. I could have made a fortune selling it in my health food store.

Woody Allen